W9-CNN-631

A BOOK ABOUT CHAPBOOKS

The People's Literature of Bygone Times

By

HARRY B. WEISS

With Illustrations

FOLKLORE ASSOCIATES, INC.
HATBORO, PENNSYLVANIA
1969

PREFACE

This book was first published a quarter of a century ago in an edition of only 100 copies. At that times chapbooks were of little interest to the general public and only a few librarians, collectors, and bookdealers had actually seen a chapbook and knew what such books were all about. Over the years these little books have gained in appreciation among students of folklore and of the development of society, reflecting as they do the vulgar manners, intellectual interests, beliefs, living conditions, entertainments, etc., of past social groups.

The present work on the people's literature of former times should be considered only as a brief introduction to an inexhaustible subject. For this reprint edition, in addition to this revised Preface, I have supplied a list containing the sources of the illustrations found herein and an addendum to the Bibliography at the end of the work.

It is a pleasure to record my obligation to Walter N. H. Harding, a fellow collector from whose extensive knowledge I was supplied with many facts. And I am greatly indebted also, for bibliographical, biographical and other information, to the late Dr. Harry M. Lydenberg, former Director of the New York Public Library; the late Clarence S. Brigham, former Director of the American Antiquarian Society; Robert W. G. Vail, former Librarian of the American Antiquarian Society; V. Valta Parma, former Curator, Rare Book Collection, Library of Congress; the late John A. Fairley, Lauriston Castle, Edinburgh; Elsie A. Russ, Deputy Librarian of the Municipal Libraries of Bath; Charles Novell, Chief Librarian of the Manchester Public Libraries; Basil Anderton, Chief Librarian of the Public Library of Newcastle-upon-Tyne; and H. M. Cashmore, City Librarian of the Birmingham Public Libraries.

For permission to use the illustrations credited to them, my thanks are extended to the late Dr. A. S. W. Rosenbach, The New York Public Library, and the American Antiquarian Society.

H. B. Weiss

CONTENTS

SOURCES OF ILLUSTRATIONS

Figure 1, page 3. From <u>Chap-Books of the Eighteenth Century</u>, by John
    Ashton, London, 1882.

Figures 2 and 3, pages 4 and 5. From "Art Among the Ballad Mongers,"
    by Llewellyn Jewitt, <u>The Art Journal</u>, London, Volumes XVII and
    XVIII, new series, 1878, 1879.

Figure 4, page 9. Title page of an Italian sixteenth century chapbook.
    (Courtesy of New York Public Library)

Figure 5, page 13. From <u>The Collected Writings of Dougal Graham</u>, by
    George MacGregor, Glasgow, 1883, Volume I.

Figure 6, page 14. From <u>The Life of Thomas Gent, Printer of York</u>, by
    Thomas Gent, London, 1832.

Figure 7, page 16. From a two volume set of the collected works of
    Hannah More, printed I believe (I no longer have the books) in
    the early 19th century.

Figure 8, page 32. From <u>The Pilgrim's Progress From This World to That
    Which is to Come</u>, Glasgow, n.d., published by Orr and Sons.

Figure 9, page 32. Title page from <u>The Worthy Sayings of Old Mr. Dod</u>,
    Market-Harborough, 1797, printed by W. Harrod.

Figure 10, page 34. Title page from a Cheap Repository Tract, <u>The Beg-
    garly Boy</u>, London, n.d., printed by J. Evans and Co.

Figure 11, page 36. Title page of <u>The Art of Swimming Rendered Easy;
    with Directions to Learners</u>, Glasgow, n.d.

Figure 12, page 39. From <u>Goldsmith's History of the Kings and Queens
    of England</u>, London, n.d., published by J. Catnach.

Figure 13, page 40. From <u>The History of the Royal Martyr King Charles
    the First</u>, sold in Bow Church Yard, London, n.d.

Figure 14, page 40. Title page of <u>The History of Mary Queen of Scots</u>,
    Newcastle-on-Tyne, n.d., published by John Ross.

Figures 15 and 16, pages 42 and 43. Pages from <u>The Pictorial History
    of London</u>, London, n.d., published by J. Catnach.

Figure 17, page 45. Title page from <u>The Loss of the Steamship Forfar-
    shire</u>, n.p., n.d.

Figure 18, page 48. From <u>The Miracle of Miracles</u>. (Entered in the Hall
    Book according to Order), n.p., n.d.

Figure 19, page 48. From the Adventures of Bamfyeld Moore Carew, For More than Forty Years Past King of the Beggars, London, n.d.

Figure 20, page 49. Title page of The Three Misers, London, 1801.

Figure 21, page 50. Engraved frontispiece of The Three Misers, London, 1801.

Figure 22, page 52. From The Surprising Life and most Strange Adventures of Robinson Crusoe of the City of York, Mariner, London, n.d.

Figure 23, page 52. From The Fortunes and Misfortunes of Moll Flanders Who was Born in Newgate. Aldermary Church Yard, Bow Lane, London, n.d.

Figures 24 and 25, page 53. Title page and engraved frontispiece from The Imprisoned Chief, London, n.d.

Figures 26 and 27, pages 54 and 55. Title page and engraved frontispiece from The Peruvian Daemon, London, 1807.

Figure 28, page 58. Title page illustration from Jack and the Giants, Newcastle, 1711, printed by J. White.

Figure 29, page 64. From A Pleasant and delightful History of Thomas Hickathrift, Newcastle, n.d., printed by M. Angus and Son.

Figure 30, page 68. Title page from Ducks and Green Peas or The Newcastle Rider, Newcastle, n.d, printed by M. Angus and Son.

Figure 31, page 70. Title page illustration from The History of Adam Bell, Clim of the Clough, and William of Cloudeslie, Newcastle, n.d.

Figure 32, page 70. Title page from Watty & Meg; or, the Wife Reformed, Newcastle-upon-Tyne, n.d.

Figure 33, page 77. Title page from A Garland of New Songs, Newcastle-upon Tyne, n.d., printed by J. Marshall.

Figure 34, page 77. Title page from The Delights of the Spring, London, n.d., printed by J. Pitts.

Figure 35, page 79. Title page from a toy songster, The Vocalist, London, n.d., printed by J. Pitts.

Figure 36, page 79. Title page from The Berkshire Lady's Garland, Glasgow, n.d.

Figures 37, 38, and 39, pages 82 and 83. Illustrations from The World turned Upside Down or the Folly of Man exemplified, London, n.d.

Figure 40, page 86. From The History of the King and the Cobler. Printed and sold at the London and Middlesex Printing Office, 81 Shoe Lane, Holborn, n.d.

SOURCES OF ILLUSTRATIONS

Figure 41, page 86. From The Whole Life and Death of Long Meg of Westminster. Printed and Sold in Aldermary Church Yard, London, n.d.

Figure 42, page 89. Title page illustration from The Merry Tales of the
Wise Men of Gotham, Aldermary Church Yard, Bow Lane, London, n.d.

Figures 43, 44, and 45, pages 91 and 93. Illustrations from The Famous
History of Tom Thumb Wherein is declared His Marvellous Acts of
Manhood Full of Wonder and Merriment, Aldermary Church Yard,
London, n.d.

Figure 46, page 96. From The Pleasant History of Jack Horner, Newcastle,
n.d.

Figures 47 and 48, pages 97 and 98. From The Friar and Boy or the Young
Piper's Pleasant Pastime, Aldermary Church Yard, London, n.d.

Figure 49, page 100. From The History of Mother Bunch of the West containing Many Rarities out of her Golden Closet of Curiosities,
London and Middlesex Printing Office, 81 Shoe Lane, Holborn, n.d.

Figure 50, page 101. Title page from Dreamer's Oracle, London, n.d.,
printed by J. Catnach.

Figures 51 and 52, page 102. From The Circle of Fate; or, True Norwood
Gipsey, London, n.d., printed by J. Catnach.

Figure 53, page 103. Title page from Old Harry, The Raree-Show-Man,
London, n.d., printed by J. Bysh.

Figure 54, page 104. From The History Of the Learned Friar Bacon, Aldermary Church Yard, London, n.d.

Figures 55 and 56, pages 105 and 106. From The History of Dr. John
Faustus shewing How he sold himself to the Devil to have power to
do what he pleased for twenty-four years, Aldermary Church Yard,
Bow Lane, London, n.d.

Figures 57, 58, and 59, pages 108 and 109. From The History of Mother
Shipton, Aldermary Church Yard, London, n.d.

Figure 60, page 109. From Nixon's Cheshire Prophecy, Aldermary Church
Yard, Bow Lane, London, n.d.

Figures 61 and 62, pages 113 and 114. Cover page and illustration from
The History of George Barnwell, London, c. 1845, published by
A. Ryle & Co.

Figure 63, page 114. From the Life of Jack Sheppard, London, c. 1825,
printed by J. Catnach.

Figure 64, page 115. Cover page of The Life of Turpin, London, n.d.,
printed by J. Catnach.

SOURCES OF ILLUSTRATIONS

Figure 65, page 116. From <u>The Life and Adventures of Richard Turpin</u>, London, c. 1820, printed by J. Catnach.

Figure 66, page 119. Title page from <u>The Fashionable Letter Writer</u>, London, n.d., printed by A. Ryle & Co.

Figure 67, page 120. Title page from cheap tract <u>Awful Phenomena of Nature!</u>, Dunfermline, 1828, printed by John Miller.

Figure 68, page 126. Title page from <u>The Most Delightful History of the King and the Cobler</u>, Boston, n.d., published by Thomas and John Fleet.

Figure 69, page 127. Title page of <u>The Prodigal Daughter</u>, Boston, c. 1771, published by Isaiah Thomas. (Courtesy of Dr. A. S. W. Rosenbach)

Figure 70, page 130. Title page from <u>A Narrative of the Sufferings, and Surprizing Deliverance of William and Elizabeth Fleming</u>, Philadelphia, 1756, printed by James Chattin. (Courtesy of New York Public Library)

Figure 71, page 132. Title page of <u>The Crafty Princess, or Golden Bull</u>, Leominster, Massachusetts, n.d., printed for Chapman Whitcomb.

Chapter 1

CHAPBOOKS AND CHAPMEN

Devils and angels, scoundrels and heroes, love and hate, murders, deathbed statements, witchcraft, riddles, tragedy, romance, song, jests, fairy tales, religion, shipwrecks, confessions, fables, hymns, speeches, executions, and all that goes to make up life, real and unreal, are reflected in the ephemeral chapbooks that once circulated so freely and are now so scarce.

The term chapbook may include anything from a broadside to a good-sized book-- anything printed--that was carried for sale by a chapman into villages, hamlets, towns. Although they varied in size, the small ones, as a rule, being intended for children, the majority were about 5½ by 3½ inches in size and contained from 4 to 24 pages, but there was really nothing fixed about their size or about the number of their pages. Selling for amounts ranging from a few farthings to a shilling, they were distributed by thousands, going into numerous homes and constituting the only reading matter of the family. The printing, in many cases, was execrable, the paper even worse, and the wood-cut illustrations, some of which did duty for various tales regardless of their fitness, were sometimes worse than the type, paper, and presswork combined. However, for many years, they carried the work of historians, poets, story-tellers, fortune-tellers, song-writers, clergymen, politicians, biographers, jesters, etc., etc., to the people, and as such, they were useful, entertaining, and instructive, despite their crudeness and their frequent deviation from accuracy and good taste.

Sometimes chapbooks were excellently printed, but more often they were not. The earliest ones were uniform in size and consisted of a 24-page single sheet duodecimo. The paper was coarse, dirty gray or whitish brown, and the woodcuts were crude and bold. Later ones of typical form consisted of a single sheet folded into 4, 8 or 16 leaves, and coverless. More often than not, they were without dates, so they could be sold for years. While many carried the names of publishers or printers, just as many contained the statement, "Printed for the Booksellers." Chapbook printers and publishers took all kinds of liberties with titles, text, and illustrations. Expediency was the rule and without hesitation these printers stole the productions of rival presses.

The early chapman was a peddler, with a long pack, partly open, suspended from his neck. In this pack, he had chapbooks, almanacs, and other small wares. He was licensed and in old laws he was referred to as a hawker, vendor chapman and unruly person. Frequently he was chased by dogs and slept with the pigs or in the barn. In later times he was somewhat dignified by the names Traveling or Flying or Running Stationer. These hawkers, peddlers, flying-stationers, or chapmen were the only merchants in rural districts in early times. To such districts, the chapman was a welcome visitor, bringing as he did, his contacts with the outside world, news, new suggestions, new things for the people to think and talk about, in addition to his stock of chap-books, trinkets, ribbons, laces, brooches, etc. Although many were knaves and were regarded with suspicion, chapmen usually were welcome, not only because of the contents of their packs, but because of their fund of gossip. Perhaps the chapman was the prototype of our Yankee peddler of one hundred or more years ago.

The name "chapman" which was used early in the fifteenth century, is apparently derived from the Anglo Saxon ceapman (trade + man) meaning a tradesman, and chapbooks were apparently books sold to the trade. It has been suggested by some that the prefix "chap" originally meant "to cheap or cheapen," hence cheap books.

When markets were held in towns and cities, stances were set apart to be occupied by chapmen. There are many references to this practice in the old records of

Scottish burghs. Sometimes the chapmen of a locality formed an organization or "Fraternity," with numerous rules for their conduct and government and with penalties for their non-observance. Funds were invested and held for distribution to needy members of the organization.

In "Round the Grange Farm; or Good Old Times," by Miss Jean L. Wilson, published in Edinburgh in 1872, the conventional Scotch chapman was described as a "middle sized, broad-shouldered man, with a keen, pawky eye, and a very sleek, worldly face. He was always clad in a blue coat like a large surtout, with big metal buttons, homespun grey vest and trousers, while his head was surmounted by a huge broad bonnet with a red top; round his neck he wore a green and yellow Indian neckerchief, which encircled his unbleached shirt collar. The lappels of his coat and vest pockets were the only fanciful parts of his dress; his pack was tied in a linen table-cover, and slung over his shoulders. His stock consisted, perhaps of hardware goods, comprising fine bawbee knives, needles, pins of all sizes, thimbles, scissors, bone combs, specks; also ballads such as 'Gill Morice' and 'Sir James the Rose,' or four-and eight-page pamphlets generally comprehending among the number 'John Cheap the Chapman,' 'The King and the Cobbler,' and 'Ali-Baba; or the Forty Thieves.' He had his regular 'rounds' which he traversed twice, or it might be many times a year; usually contriving at nightfall to reach some friendly farmhouse, where the cog of porridge and bed of straw were cheerfully given in return for his budget of news, his packet of chapbooks, or small parcel of tea and sugar, bespoken on his last visit."

Various road-books, travelers' companions, guides, almanacs, etc., were available to chapmen and contained information about fairs, stage-coach schedules, distances between towns, etc. Road-books of a sort existed in Great Britain as early as 1570 and as time went on, the number of them increased and their information became more detailed and complete. Some of them were designed to appeal particularly to chapmen and one such was entitled "The City and Countrey Chapman's Almanack For the Year of our Lord 1687." This is a short title. As a matter of fact, the remainder of the title specified the contents as containing a list of the fairs and markets of England and Wales, and their dates, post roads, names of market times, etc.,".....With other things useful for all sorts of Traders or Chapmen whatsoever." This road-book was published in London in 1686.

Still another example was "The Traveller's and Chapman's Daily Instructor," printed in London in 1705 for G. Sawbridge at the Three Flower-de-Luces in Little Brittain. This contains "The High-Ways and Roads, and how to Travel from one Place to another. The Market-Towns and the Days of the Week whereon they are kept. All the Fairs in England, Scotland and Ireland; the Time and Places when and where held, more at large by some Thousands, and truer than heretofore hath ever been done by any one Author." And in addition there is information on distances between towns, on stage-coaches and their running time, and on "the Places and Signs of the Inns," where the coaches stopped. New editions of some of the road-books were brought out at regular intervals over a period of years. Ireland too had its road-books.

Originally all literature was oral. With the beginning of reading and writing there came into existence a literature, possessed exclusively by the cultivated classes, and this has come down to us in the shape of beautiful manuscripts on vellum. With the introduction of printing some of these texts found their way into print and eventually publishing became an established business. At first only the well-to-do could afford books and the uncultivated had only the literature of oral tradition. Along with the development of printing there had been an increase in learning among the masses and many knew how to read and write. So a natural demand arose for cheap entertainment of a literary sort and this was met by printing broadsides, ballads and chapbooks. The contents of chapbooks were selected from books that contained material likely to suit popular taste and the accounts were usually greatly curtailed. Much of the unliterary material was supplied by annonymous authors and unliterary hacks.

In 1873 Professor John Fraser called attention to the vulgar manners, popular jokes, songs, national characteristics, and living conditions of low Scottish life that were reflected in the contents of Scottish chapbooks. For example, carriages and carts are not mentioned in eighteenth century chapbooks, for the simple reason that they did not exist. People either rode on horseback or walked over beaten tracks that passed for roads. And in "Jockie and Maggie's Courtship," printed after 1750, Jockie and his mother visit a friend; "Jockie mounts an', his mither behind him, trots awa' till coming down the brae aboon John Davie's well, the auld beast being unferry o' the feet, she foundered before, the girth an' curple brake. Jockie tumbled o'er her lugs, an' his mither out o'er him, in the well wi' a slunge."

Figure 1

A Chapman
From "The Cries and Habits of the City of London"
By M. Lauron, 1709

Highway robberies, black-mail and cattle stealing were common and many chapbooks were devoted to accounts of violence and bloodshed, as are witnessed by such titles as "The Female Robber," "The Bloody Gardner," "Jack Shepherd," "Dick Turpin," "The Irish Assassin," etc. The superstition and beliefs in charms, dreams, fortune telling, and witchcraft went hand-in-hand with chapbooks on the same subjects.

The Church and the Law were harsh and severe. People were executed for misdemeanors that are nowadays punished by short jail sentences and the authority of the Church found its way into all phases of domestic life. Even private and domestic life were conducted with severity. Children were ruled with the rod and the same conditions prevailed in the schools. All through the chapbooks of the period these conditions are reflected. Drunkenness, gambling, immorality, cock-fighting, ungodly songs, rude jokes, profanity, religious rites were all a part of life and of the chapbooks too. "The Coalman's Courtship" only repeated what might be heard in any small village.

The custom of entire households living all in a heap in one room, the general use of ale, the license allowed at weddings, fairs, and the practice of "bedding" young couples and "touzzling" among the hay all parade true to form through the literature of the chapbook. However, the flood of chapbooks also carried the stories and songs with which the literature of Scotland is enriched, and in addition foreign tales were stolen and then abridged and adapted to local conditions. What has just been said of Scottish chapbooks applies more or less to the chapbook literature of all countries.

The illustrations that decorated the people's literature during the sixteenth, seventeenth and eighteenth centuries were frequently grotesque and startling. At least they now seem so to us. These early woodcut illustrations, however, seem to fit in with the worn types, dingy paper, and the poor press work that went into the manufacture of chapbooks and broadside ballads, and certainly their readers found nothing to criticize. The illustrations adorning ballad sheets and chapbooks were not always intended to illustrate the text. Their readers expected some decoration and the printer supplied it the best he could. It certainly would not have been economic to have a new cut made for each series of broadsides. Chapbooks had to be "embellished" so far as possible "with elegant cuts," and type cuts, founts and presses passed from one printer to another. It is not surprising, therefore, to find the same illustrations used for completely different subjects. This is one of the amusing features of chapbook illustrations.

In the black letter ballads, or those printed from a thick, old English type, used until about 1700, many of the wood cuts were made with some fidelity and as a result, they portray information on various historical and other points even though they have a flatness, and are frequently incorrectly drawn, and rude in execution. Various subjects connected with the manners, customs, costumes and home life of people now gone are illustrated more or less in the old broadside ballads. During James' reign ballads were collected into garlands or small, eight-page chapbooks, with a woodcut on the title page. In 1543 a proclamation was issued against "foolish books, ballads, rhymes and other lewd treatises in the English tonge" so that true religion might be advanced, and later there were other edicts against them.

During most of the eighteenth century chapbook illustrations seemed to become cruder than ever. Old cuts were getting worn from constant use and even new illustrations were crudely drawn and entirely lacking in anything except grotesqueness. This

Figure 2

The Dragon of Wantley
From a black-letter broadside

period was followed by one which began during the last quarter of the century in which John and Thomas Bewick's wood engravings frequently appeared, especially in children's chapbooks. Many chapbooks in prose and verse were devoid of illustrations and this was especially true of garlands. Such ones, however, were frequently embellished on the title page, either by a small woodcut or by various printer's ornaments. Regardless of the crudeness of chapbook illustrations, they have a certain charm and quaintness and seem to be an integral part of the chapbook itself. Without illustrations many chapbooks would be dull and dreary.

Figure 3

Captain Dangerfield in the Pillory
From a black-letter broadside

During the latter part of the eighteenth century and the first quarter of the nineteenth, large numbers of chapbooks were issued with engraved frontispieces, frequently colored. Sometimes these were folding frontispieces either plain or colored. And children's chapbooks issued at this time frequently contained colored illustrations in the text, green, red, blue and yellow sometimes put on with little regard as to whether the colors overlapped correctly or not. London seemed to be the chief source of chapbooks with engraved frontispieces, but on the other hand there were many provincial towns also, from which they were issued.

Chapter 2

CHAPBOOKS IN SCOTLAND, ENGLAND AND OTHER COUNTRIES

Although exact limits are difficult to define, the Scottish chapbook period may be said to have extended from 1638 to 1830, though the chief impetus came from the Revolution of 1688. Even before this, or in 1644, Zachary Boyd, one-time minister of the Barony Parish of Glasgow and vice-chancellor of the University, complained to the General Assembly about the "idle books,......fables, love-songs, baudry ballads, heathen husks, youth's poison," in circulation. From the time of the Revolution their numbers gradually increased down to 1746, when Dougal Graham published his metrical "History of the Rebellion." Graham's contributions to chapbook literature were new and outstanding and as a result chapbooks became even more popular. By 1775 they had reached their peak and for the next fifty years their popularity continued unabated. However, following this period they began to decay. Nothing new was added and other cheap literature crowded them out. Some publishers continued to turn out so-called "new and improved" series, but times had changed and popular taste had improved.

Chapbooks were issued from many towns in Scotland and at one time their annual circulation was said to be 200,000. The leading (and wheezy) presses were to be found in Glasgow, Stirling, Falkirk, Edinburgh, Paisley, Dunbar, etc., and chapbook printers were to be found also in Airdrie, Fintray, Greenock, Kilmarnock, Kirkintilloch, Newton-Stewart, Peterhead, Stirling and other Scottish towns. The names of various printers appear on extant Scottish chapbooks now in the hands of collectors, in spite of the large number that carry no names and no place of publication. In Glasgow, some of these were Thomas Duncan, Robert and Andrew Foulis, R. Hutchison, J. Lumsden & Son, J. & M. Robertson, Francis Orr and Sons, etc. In Stirling, there were J. Fraser, E. Johnstone, J. Neilson, W. Macnie, C. Randall, M. Randall, etc. In Falkirk, T. Johnston published many. In Edinburgh there were Archibald Martin, J. Morren, James Murray, J. Stewart, Francis M'Cartney, etc. In Paisley, Caldwell and Sons, G. Caldwell, and J. Neilson were active as producers of chapbooks. In Dunbar, there was George Miller. And so-- the lists could be extended to other towns.

In England, chapbooks appeared during the sixteenth century, and were popular during the reign of Elizabeth. The earliest ones were printed in black-letter and illustrated by wood engravings, the best of which were supposedly engraved in Germany or in the Netherlands. These small quarto English chapbooks originated from the black-letter tracts of Wynkyn de Worde, Copland, etc., and some were finely printed. The poorer, penny ones of popular taste did not appear much before 1700, according to Ashton.

London was the chief production center of English chapbooks, and many were issued from shops on the Old London Bridge. During the course of time various towns, such as Bristol, York, Newcastle, etc., became prolific producers of chapbooks. To these and to other centers of production, the chapman flocked for their supplies. About the middle of the eighteenth century, chapbooks were somewhat out of favor, although their complete disappearance did not take place until well into the nineteenth century. Eighteenth-century chapbooks were inferior, both as to printing and literary character, in comparison with those of the preceding century.

Some of the English towns where supplies for the chapmen were printed are Alnwick, Aylesbury, Banbury, Bath, Bicester, Birmingham, Bristol, Cambridge, Carlisle, Chipping Norton, Coventry, Derby, Epsom, Exeter, Gateshead, Greenwich, Hull, Ipswich, Kendal, Liverpool, London, Manchester, Newcastle, Nottingham, Otley, Oxford, Penrith, St. Ives, Salisbury, Scarborough, Sheffield, Tewksbury, Whitehaven, Worcester, York, etc. And there were others.

Numerous were the chapbook printers in London, many of whom issued chapbooks with engraved and colored frontispieces, and with hand colored illustrations in the text. Mr. Harding's collection of chapbooks with engraved frontispieces alone embraces examples from over eighty different London firms, from about 1785 to 1830. Individual printers and various partnerships that seemed to last, for the most part, only a few years, participated in the enormous output. Chapbooks with colored frontispieces seem to be in direct descent from those issued in the 1780s and 1790s by T. Sabine, J. Hollis, and C. Sheppard. At that time they ran from 36 to 60 or more pages with a plain, woodcut frontispiece, and they were in some cases printed on rough, blue-toned paper, made famous by Pitts a few years later. With the turn of the century, there was an improvement in the quality of the paper and the frontispieces were engraved and sometimes colored. During the period 1810 to 1820, the number of pages seemed to become more or less standardized at from 24 to 36 pages, with W. Mason, J. Bailey, R. Harrild, T. Hughes, and J. Ker being the chief printers. About 1817 J. Bysh and Dean and Munday appeared on the scene. Colored folding frontispieces occurred in a few song books in the early 1800s, but did not seem to come into general use in prose chapbooks until about 1815. Dean and Munday, and for a few years, J. Bailey continued to issue a large number of chapbooks during the 1820-1830 period, but the chief publishers seem to have been Fairburn, and Coles and Hodgson.

Outside of London, Thomas Richardson of Derby was the chief producer of chapbooks with colored, folding frontispieces. They appeared with engraved frontispieces at Banbury, Blackburn, Hull, Gainsborough, Lambeth, New castle and Stourbridge from 1800 to 1830 and later, but seemed to go out of fashion in the 1830s. Many of the illustrations appearing in these productions were made by Heath, Rowlandson and one or the other of the Cruikshanks.

In comparison with English and Scottish chapbooks, Irish chapbooks are scarce and little seems to be recorded about them. In Dublin, it is known that B. Corcoran produced some from 1767 to 1778, and R. Kinnier was in the business probably about 1775. Cheap Repository Tracts were printed in Dublin by B. Dugdale, William Watson and Son about 1795 and by William Watson II from 1805 to 1818. A "History of Reynard the Fox," was printed in Dublin in 1738. Religious and other chapbooks were also printed by Richard Grace, Richard Grace and Son, and Richard Grace and Sons from 1818 to 1836, all in Dublin, and James Henry North, wholesale ironmonger of 7 Old Church Street, Dublin, published chapbook songsters. In Belfast, James Magee printed many that are dated from 1754 to 1770. In Newry there was Dan. Carpenter in 1767-68 and also George Harrison about the same time, and in Waterford, Jer. Caldwell was in business about 1775.

From 1816 to the middle thirties the following towns with their chapbook printers may be noted: Monaghan, G. Gass, West, Greacen; Limerick, S. B. Goggin; Belfast, J. Smyth; Dublin, R. Grace, T. Caldwell; Waterford, W. Kelly; Omagh, Flying Stationers; Drogheda, Flying Stationers; and it is known that about 1805, printers in Armagh, Lugan, and Londonderry were turning out Irish political chapbooks, as well as others. Chapbooks with engraved fronitspieces are known with the following imprints: Dublin, A. O'Neil, 1814-1816; William Porter, 1803; J. Carrick, 1818; Cork, Edwards & Savage, 1810. In years to come there is no doubt that the above meager information will be greatly extended.

Many chapbook printers and publishers turned out along with their chapbooks, large numbers of song sheets, or "Garlands," or broadside ballads, and in addition many sold children's penny books, tops, marbles, handbills, etc. The earlier ballad sheets were quite large and sometimes the songs were printed the long way of the paper. At the end of the eighteenth and the beginning of the nineteenth centuries many appeared looking like galley proofs. Later on, some appeared in sheets nearly three feet long with three or four columns of type. Such ballad sheets printed on one side were hung up in alehouses and other places where people gathered and thousands were worn out of existence. The publishers of books and weightier things usually looked down upon the printers of chapbooks and garlands, which they considered as trivial, but nowadays these trivial things are much desired.

It is recorded that chapbooks first appeared in France shortly after the invention of the printing press and that by the end of the fifteenth century they were fairly numerous.

In Paris in 1854 there was published a work, in two fat volumes, copiously illustrated, entitled "Histoire des livres populaires; ou, De la littérature du colportage, depuis le xve siècle jusqu' a l'établissement de la Commission d'examen des livres du colportage," by Charles Nisard. For nearly three centuries France had been flooded with chapbooks and other works of a popular kind, through colporteurs or peddlers and in 1852 a commission was named to examine such reading matter critically, with the idea of publicly calling attention to the dangerous influence or uselessness of some of the little books and of the bad influence they could have upon the customs and spirit of the people. Of course along with this, the commission was in favor of only useful and moral books and believed that they should forbid the sale of three-fourths of the literature of colportage in the interest of workers and country people, groups easily led astray. However, for the benefit of learned people, collectors, bibliophiles, etc., the commission believed that a record of the books, good and bad, should be preserved. And so we have the two excellent volumes on the history of chapbooks in France, showing the intellectual diversions of the people for two or three centuries. Mr. Nisard's work includes many little books and works that ordinarily are not classed as chapbooks by collectors, but this does not detract from the interest of his two volumes. In fact it adds to it.

French chapbooks, in the range of their subjects, did not differ much from those of other countries. The almanacs, many of which were printed in Paris, Nancy and Troyes, contained, in addition to their usual astronomical contents, prophecies, cabalistic devices, anecdotes, jokes, astrology, divination by dreams, language of the flowers, notices of famous people, accounts of battles, travels, proverbs, maxims, history, religion, popular statistics, songs, fiction, etc. Most of them contained illustrations. Their dirty gray paper combined with their typography made them hideous examples of the art of printing, although there were some exceptions. Without going deeply into the contents of French chapbooks it may be said that their subjects included magic, divination, which was more popular than magic, domestic economy, veterinary medicine such as it was, rules for card games, bad advice relative to conjugal love, puns and jokes, many of them indelicate and not at all uplifting, dialogues, catechisms, including those for lovers, discourses, funeral eulogies, burlesque sermons, histories of statesmen and robbers, biographies including the popular Wandering Jew, Till Eulenspiegel, the chronicles of the great and enormous Gargantua, religion, morals, spiritual canticles, including stories and lives of patriarchs and saints, epistles such as popular directions for writing business, complimentary, and love letters, slang, education, and novels, stories and tales which comprised a considerable part of the literature of colportage. As usual, only about one in fifty of the chapbooks, considered by the French Commission, bore a name or date. Mr. Nisard's account is invaluable to collectors, bringing together, as it does, examples of the types of chapbooks that flourished in France from the fifteenth century to 1854.

One of the purposes of Mr. Nisard's volumes was to hold up to public view the good, moral and truly pleasing chapbooks to serve as models for those who might undertake to regenerate the industry of colportage. However, chapbooks disappeared in France just as they did in other countries, through the influx of cheap literature of other types and because of changed popular taste.

In Italy in the sixteenth century there were Popular Tracts and Romances of Chivalry and also Rappresentazioni Sacre, both groups illustrated with wood-cuts typical of the Florentine school. These may be considered as chapbooks, and even as late as the beginning of the twentieth century, there appeared from the printing office of Adriano Salani in Florence, cheap literature that could be classed as chapbooks. A translation of Hamlet, the Decamerone, tales of crime, history, prayers, dialogues, songs, Bible history, descriptions of miracles, etc., could be purchased for a few pennies. A strong

¶ POMPE ET CERIMONIE CELEBRATE NELLA
INCLITA CIPTA DI FIORENZA NELLA FE
STIVITA DEL PRECVRSORE IOHAN
NI BAPTISTA LANNO . M . D . X IIII.

¶CYNTHIA.

E L rembōbāre fragor delle spie armi
chi sturbō Marte i celo al fero aspecto
le uoce popu'ar / gli audaci armi
che a loue mouon di letitia il pecto   Propositione
le pōpe sculpte i saldi / & forti marmi
che son dantiqua gloria alto subiecto
hoggi sforzan uogar la debil naue
del mio thusco arno / londe alte / & soaue

Se dunq adscende dello arguto ple tro   Inuocatione
el resonante accento alsom no cielo
mentre che temoto il belligero sceptro
aspira Apollo il furor del tuo Delo
qñdi eburno : aur : geme i de rostro : helect
orneran le corni : gli adyti / e il uelo (ro
corone : incensi / & lumi / a i sacri altari
spatgera Pan / col suo zufol dispari

Figure 4

Title Page of an Italian, Sixteenth Century Chapbook
Courtesy of the New York Public Library

religious element appears in this popular literature, which although often crude and coarse, is free from licentiousness. These twentieth century Italian chapbooks, are for the most part, ghosts of a former chapbook age. Stories of priests, narratives of crime and scandal, the story of an unnatural mother who throws her little daughter into a fire, an account of the unhappy end of a courtesan who is slain by the man she loves, the cruelty of a woman who poisoned twenty-three children, the exploits of Antonio Crocco, a brigand who terrorized Naples, an explanation of the good and evil influences of the planets upon the birth of men and women, debates between poor men and rich men, between bachelors and married men, love, marriage, humor, songs of all sorts, games; all of these topics come to light in these twentieth century Italian chapbooks.

Germany had its chapbooks, printed by firms in Wein, Hamburg, Frankfurt, Leipzig, Reutlinger, Cologne, Augsburg, Halle, etc., etc., and their subjects and dates or lack of dates correspond more or less with those of chapbooks of other countries. In early times when the weaving was done in rooms in rural sections, there appeared Rockenbuchlein or Weaving Booklets, containing folksongs, dance songs, verses, riddles, tricks, etc., for the enjoyment of the people when they were gathered together. Translations of French folklore circulated in chapbook form, and there finally appeared on the scene fables, humor, romance, songs and the varied popular subjects so common to chapbooks.

China, too, had its chapbooks and within comparatively recent times, rudely printed, popular literature could be purchased in Swatow, at any bookstall, for small sums. Plays and ballads dealing with actual and imaginary happenings, local and historical; unhappy lovers, war, spelling, sermons, the evils of gambling and opium smoking, Heaven as an object of worship, fairies, etc., all designed for instruction, amusement, and moral suasion, give on an idea of their contents. According to Maclagan this popular literature was "largely steeped in immorality."

It should, perhaps, be stated here, that the earliest European chapbooks with their romances of chivalry, religious plays, and poems of knighthood, illustrated by wood engravings, were not by any means intended for the lower classes. These were not poorly printed like their successors, and their circulation, no doubt, took place among notables, scholars and rich townspeople. It was only after the art of printing became well established, and reading more general, that the chapbook flourished in all its glory, with its abbreviated tales and other changes necessary for wider circulation among uncultured classes.

In the Netherlands, the chapbook or volksboek, embraced the literature of the lower classes as it existed until the beginning of the nineteenth century. The early chapbooks of the fifteenth and sixteenth centuries first contained passion plays, Dutch songs, and old chivalrous novels in verse, true to the hand-written accounts, but the sixteenth century brought a complete change in literary tastes, and with the printed word flourishing and under the influence of the classics, chapbooks as they originally started out, were pushed into the background and becomes more and more the literature of the lower classes. The printing became bad, also the spelling; the paper was cheap; the illustrations frequently had no connection with the text and the contents were sadly abbreviated. Some originated from old Dutch poems and prose and others were adapted from those in foreign languages. The most widely known chapbooks originated from Middle Netherlands novels. In addition to such contents as have been noted, Dutch chapbooks, like their foreign relatives, carried popular accounts of travels, fortune-telling, street songs, apparitions of the devil, crimes of highwaymen, lives of the saints, witchcraft, magic, etc.

What has been said of the chapbook in the European countries that have been mentioned, could be extended to include other countries. Spain has not been mentioned specifically, but it is needless to state that chapbooks flourished here too and the fifty some titles of Spanish chapbooks listed in the "Catalogue of the Chapbooks of the New York Public Library," indicate the types of their contents.

It may be said that, except for certain kinds of folklore connected with particular countries, the contents of chapbooks, the world over, fall readily into certain classes and many were the borrowings, with of course, adaptations and changes to suit particular countries.

Chapter 3

CHAPBOOK AUTHORS

The title of this chapter is somewhat misleading. For the most part, chapbooks are authorless, and the authorship of many of our folk tales and popular stories of our ancestors is lost in antiquity. And in addition the personages whose exploits are set forth in chapbooks may be either real or fictitious. In most cases they are probably the latter. No one knows who wrote "The Pleasant and Delightful History of Jack and the Giants." Folk-tale happenings are widely distributed. Carried from one tribe to another and from one country to another, and from one continent to another, there is often in the tale little intraneous evidence to indicate the origin either of native or foreign parts. European folk-tales are said to be remarkably uniform in content, although differing in speech and local color. The frameworks of folk-tales and myths are almost exclusively made up of events that reflect the occurrences of human life, especially those that agitate the emotions. The extremely fanciful character of the tales may be ordinary wishes or amplifications of our experiences, such as the smallness of dwarfs, bigness of giants or manifestations of objects of fear. Man has a limited power of imagination and the tendency is to use the old stock of inventive occurrences rather than to think up new ones. The highly embroidered and more complex locally colored tales are the result of more thought and attention given to them by priests, poets and deeply interested persons.

However, in spite of the fact that chapbooks are mainly authorless, there were a few tales and pieces that were published under an author's name and in other cases, although the writings may have been published anonymously, it is definitely known who wrote them. This is particularly true of some of the contents of the little chapbooks for children, that appeared late in the chapbook era. In still other cases the writings of well-known authors have been incorporated in chapbooks without their consent or knowledge. It may be noted here that of the 1,200 chapbooks that I examined in the New York Public Library, the names of only about fifty authors were indicated thereon. This shows their scarcity.

Many persons have heard of Alexander Wilson, the ornithologist, and many are familiar with his monumental "American Ornithology." Many may also know that he wrote poetry, but hardly any connect him with Scottish chapbook literature. Wilson was born at Paisley, Scotland, in 1766. At the age of thirteen he was bound to a weaver and following his apprenticeship, he worked at his trade, peddled ladies' goods, wrote poems and was keenly alive and receptive to the impressions made by his contacts with various types of people and with his surroundings. At the age of 24 the first edition of his poems was published at Paisley by his friend John Neilson, "for the author," but the volume had no sale and he was unable to pay his friend. This was in 1790. The second edition that appeared in 1791 was only the large remainder of the first, with a new title page and a few additions and omissions.

His first success came with the publication of his "Wattey and Meg" in 1792. This appeared as a chapbook and was very popular. Because his ideas of democracy did not seem possible of attainment in Scotland, Wilson sailed for America in 1794. For a while he worked with a printer in Philadelphia. Later he was employed at weaving, peddling in New Jersey, teaching school at various places, and surveying, drawing and planning his "Ornithology."

Wilson wrote some 126 poems, but not all of them appeared in chapbooks. However, "Rab and Ringan: a tale To which is added Verses occasioned by seeing two men sawing timber in an open field, in defiance of a furious storm," by Alexander Wilson, was published at Paisley in 1827 by G. Caldwell in chapbook form. "Rab and Ringan" is a tale on the question, "Whither is diffidence, or the allurements of pleasure, the greatest bar to progress in knowledge." Wilson's "The Loss o' the Pack," another familiar title in chapbook literature, was published at Penrith by Anthony Soulby and also at Paisley by G. Caldwell, in both cases, along with other poems not by Wilson. In addition to being published at Paisley, Wilson's "Wattey and Meg, or the wife reformed," was utilized by other chapbook publishers in Glasgow and Falkirk. In the "Paisley Repository, No. III," a sort of serial chapbook, appeared Wilson's "Hardyknute, A Heroic Scottish Ballad." John Millar, bookseller of Sandholes, Paisley, appears to have been the editor of the "Repository" which was printed by different printers including Andrew Young and J. Neilson. In the "Repository" No. viii [1810], its entire four pages are devoted to Alexander Wilson and titles of 18 of his poems, some written in Scotland and others in America. For the most part, Wilson's literary writings are of small interest to anyone except certain students. His "The Pack nas been characterized as a dreary dialogue between a peddler and his pack and many others of his poems as trivial and without merit. However, "Wattey and Meg" is a fine bit of work and several of his verses about birds are of considerable merit.

Wilson's fame rests more securely upon his "Ornithology" than upon his poetry, but the fact remains that he started out as a chapman and became famous, something that few chapmen managed to accomplish.

Another chapbook author and chapman too, who has had more written about him than any similar personage, was Dougal Graham, one time skellat bellman of Glasgow. In spite of his popularity as a biographical subject, it appears that little that is authentic is really known about him, and all that he ever made known about himself is contained in some verses entitled, "An Account of the Author," which were prefixed to the first edition of his "History of the Rebellion," a chapbook published in Glasgow in 1746.

Various authorities have attributed to him the authorship of certain chapbooks that had a considerable degree of popularity during their life-time, and in this brief account I have followed Mr. John A. Fairley, whose monograph on "Dougal Graham and the chap-books by and attributed to him" appeared in the Records of the Glasgow Bibliographical Society in 1914. Mr. Fairley's presentation and conclusions are intelligent and logical and his paper appears to have been the last that was published, although during the intervening years, it is entirely possible that he has gathered additional data.

Dougal Graham was born in a little community situated below the castle rock of Stirling about 1724. His formal education was sparse and, when he was 21 years of age, he joined the forces of the Young Chevalier about September, 1745. It is believed that he really was a camp follower of a sort, because he was physically unfit for a soldier's life, being a hunchback, lame and undersized. He stayed with the army of Prince Charles until after Culloden when he returned to Stirling and wrote his "History of the Rebellion," which circulated as a chapbook. Before and after the 1745-46 episode, it is thought that Graham was a chapman. Local contemporary records state that a Dougall Grahame was admitted "to the freedom of the Incorporation" on September 8, 1749, these records being entitled "The Laws and Acts of the Fraternity of Chapmen in Stirling Shire."

About 1770, the exact date being unknown, Graham was appointed, after competition, to the post of skellat bellman of Glasgow, which he held until his death at Glasgow on July 20, 1779.

Although he may have written songs all his life and although many might have appeared in chapbooks, being anonymous, it is not possible to identify them. There are, however, four chapbook songs that are traditionally supposed to have been written by Graham, these being "Turnimspike," "Haud awa' frae me Donald," "John Hielandman's Remarks on Glasgow," and "Tugal M'Tagger." In addition there are approximately 20 titles, not including any that might have been added since 1914, that are associated with

Graham's name, two of these being in verse and the remainder in prose. These twenty
titles include such popular chapbook pieces as "The History of the Rebellion," "The Battle of Drummossie-Muir," "Jocky and Maggy's Courtship," "The Coalman's Courtship,"
"Lothian Tom," "John Cheap the Chapman," "Leper the Taylor," "The Witty Jokes of John
Falkirk," "John Falkirk's Cariches," "Paddy from Cork," "George Buchanan," and "Simple
John." Only the first two, both printed in 1746, the former at Glasgow, bear the name
of Graham on their title pages. Of the popular "History," there were at least ten editions, the last having been published in 1850 at Aberdeen. The third edition, of 1774,
carries a portrait of the author, as a frontispiece.

Figure 5

Dougal Graham
(Glasgow Bibliographical Society, 1912-1913)

        The anonymously published works attributed to Graham represent the best humor-
ous prose found in Scottish chapbooks. Mr. George Caldwell, a Paisley dealer of penny
histories and bawbee ballads, printed and sold many of Graham's writings and he remembered Graham as a man who could dash off a penny history in no time at all--and they always sold well, having plenty of coarse jokes to season them.

        All in all, Dougal Graham was an interesting and versatile chapman. If, as it
is supposed by some, his "History of John Cheap the Chapman" is autobiographical, then
in his own words he "was a very comical short thick fellow, with a broad face and a
large nose; both lame and lazy, and something leacherous among the lassies; he chused
rather to sit idle than work at any time, as he was a hater of hard labour. No man needed to offer him cheese and bread after he cursed he would not have it; for he would
blush at bread and milk, when hungry, as a beggar doth at a bawbee. He got the name of
John Cheap the chapman, by his selling twenty needles for a penny, and twa leather laces
for a farthing."

During the eighteenth century York was an important centre upon which the chapmen of Yorkshire depended for their supplies of chapbooks and ballads. Located here was
Thomas Gent who not only printed chapbooks, but who wrote them as well. Mr. Gent, very
thoughtfully, wrote a biography of himself, which was printed in London in 1832 and this
has been gratefully used by his various biographers.

Born in Ireland, of English parents, in 1693, Thomas Gent was, when 13 or 14
years old, apprenticed to a Dublin printer. Due to strict supervision which irked him,
he escaped to England when he was about seventeen and obtained employment in London with
a Mr. Midwinter of Pie Corner, Smithfield, who was engaged principally in printing chapbooks and broadsides. Here he became familiar with the composition of chapmen's literature. During his early years he was employed by various printers, including a Mrs.
Bradford, in Fetter Lane, a Mr. Mears in Blackfriars, and also by Mr. John White, a master printer of York, at a salary of 18 pounds per year, with board, lodging and washing.
He stayed with Mr. White only about a year, falling in love with the maid, and after a
short visit to Dublin, finally wound up in London, working at first with his former employer, Mr. Midwinter, in 1717. In 1721 he set up a press of his own in Fleet Lane and
turned out ballads and pamphlets, many composed by himself.

Aug.ᵗ Fox, sculp.

Figure 6

Thomas Gent
From "The Life of Thomas Gent, Printer of York,"
published in London, 1832.

On December 10, 1722, he married his former sweetheart, the maid with whom he
had fallen in love while in Mr. White's employ in York. During a lapse of ten years the
maid, Miss Alice Guy, had married her employer's grandson and heir and he had died leaving her a good printing establishment. Gent was now a comparatively well-fixed man with
a first-class printing business. He started a newspaper, became somewhat overbearing,
and was in constant conflict with his neighbors and townsmen. His newspaper lasted less
than four years; additional rival presses were started in York and Gent lost much of
the better class work. In 1740 he lost his house, through a legal transaction of his
wife's former husband. In 1761 his wife died and after that his business declined rap-
idly. Money became scarce and the typography and paper of his later works became

wretched. He was kept from want by being elected a pensioner of Allen's Charity and died in Petergate, May 19, 1778, at the age of 87.

Most of his London publications are lost. A list of his York productions was compiled many years ago. In "Yorkshire Chap-Books," (London, 1889) edited by Charles A. Federer, some of Gent's rather extensive chapbooks are reproduced. These are in verse and were not only written, but printed, by Thomas Gent. Some of these titles are: "British Piety Display'd in the Glorious Life, Suffering and Death of the Blessed St. Winefred," (York, 1742), this had over 80 subscribers whose names are printed on the last page, and the entire work is in five parts; "The History of the Life and Miracles of our Blessed Saviour, Jesus Christ," (York, n.d.); "Judas Iscariot," (York, 1772), this, his last production, was printed for him by a brother printer; "The Pattern of Piety: or Tryals of Patience. Being The Most Faithful Spiritual Songs of the Life and Death of the once Afflicted Job." (Scarborough, 1734); and "Piety Display'd in the Holy Life and Death Of the Antient and Celebrated St. Robert, Hermit, at Knaresborough," (York, n.d.), in prose.

Thomas Gent was the author of other works that are not chapbooks, and besides being a printer, he was a historian, poet, engraver and binder. There is no doubt of his intelligence, wide reading, and of his literary ability. His chapbooks and tracts are scarce and are rarely offered for sale.

I came near forgetting Hannah More and the Cheap Repository Tracts that came from her pen. These are usually considered as chapbooks by collectors. Mrs. More was born in 1745 and died in 1833. She was the daughter of a clergyman who lived in Hanham, near Bristol. In 1765 she moved with her four sisters to Bristol where they ran a boarding school for young ladies. She wrote a pastoral drama at the age of sixteen and a tragedy that was acted for one night at Bath. Dr. Johnson, Miss Fanny Burney and Garrick all knew Hannah More and thought highly of her. Horace Walpole called her his Holy Hannah. Her literary labors were extensive and her religious moral tracts had a wide circulation. A number of the so-called Cheap Repository Tracts were written by her and it is recorded that 2 million copies were sold the first year and more than 150,000 of one of the best of them, "The Shepherd of Salisbury Plain." She also wrote political tracts in defense of the English Constitution against the Revolutionary party.

J. Evans and Company of London were the "Printers to the Cheap Repository for Moral and Religious Tracts" and J. Marshall and R. White of the same city printed the same line on his productions. Between the two publishers, thousands of tracts were produced. In 1795 and 1796 J. Marshall advertised 22 historical titles, 20 called "Sunday Readings" and 18 titles under the heading "Poetry." All, of course, were moral and religious tales. They sold from a half-penny to three pence each and great allowance was made to shopkeepers and hawkers. Some carried the following scale of prices on the cover page: "4 s. 6 d. per 100--2 s. 6 d. for 50--1 s. 6 d. for 25." Some of the Cheap Repository titles were "Two Shoemakers," "The Lancashire Collier Girl," "The Happy Waterman," "The Beggarly Boy," "Daniel in the Den of Lions," "The Gin Shop," "Charley Jones, the Footman," "The Valley of Tears," "Sinful Sally," "A Hymn of Praise," etc.

The first "Cheap Repository Tracts" were issued by Samuel Hazard in Cheap Street, Bath, and Hannah More hired men to carry the tracts to different parts of the country. Miss More had started many Sunday schools in Somerset, where children were taught to read, and she wanted to give them moral tales on which they could exercise their accomplishments. Some of the square wood cuts on the cover pages of the Cheap Repository Tracts were engraved by John Bewick.

During the early part of the nineteenth century various publishers of children's chapbooks in America, utilized the work of English authors and we find the names of John Aiken, Anna Letitia Barbauld, Thomas Day, Ann and Jane Taylor, Priscella Wakefield, Mary M. Sherwood, Mary Belson Elliott, and others appearing on such productions.

For example H. & E. Phinney of Cooperstown, N.Y. in 1828 published extracts entitled, "The Farm-Yard Journal," from "Evenings at Home," by John Aiken and Mrs. Barbauld.

"Barbauld's Hymns" appeared under the imprint of Mahlon Day, New York, and also as
"Hymns for Little Children" under that of Samuel Wood & Sons, New York, both about 1820.
C. Shepard of New York City brought out "Little Charles," and J. S. Redfield of the
same place published "Theodore Carleton, or perseverance against ill-fortune," both
titles being by Mrs. Barbauld.

        John Aiken, a physician, and his sister, Anna Letitia Barbauld were the children
of a schoolmaster who was also a Unitarian minister. Anna married a Dissenting minister
and both kept a school at Palgrave in Suffolk. Anna wrote essays, children's books, and
edited Richardson's letters. She and her brother collaborated at times. Her children's
books are all of the "moral" type, so common during the period she wrote, and both Lamb
and Coleridge criticized her quite severely.

Figure 7

Hannah More
From an engraving by O. Pelton
after a painting by H. W. Pickersgill.

        Thomas Day, well known for his "Sanford and Merton," now considered a priggish
book, but successful when it appeared in 1783 and 1786, because everyone expected didactic stories, also appeared in children's chapbooks in America. One such was called
"The Forsaken Infant," and was printed by J. C. Totten, New York, in 1819. Day was an
enthusiastic follower of Rousseau and at one time he tried to bring up a girl on lines
following Rousseau's philosophy, with the idea of providing himself with a perfect wife.
The attempt failed and he married an heiress.

"My Mother, A Poem," and "My Sister, A Poem," both by Ann Taylor, were published by Mahlon Day of New York. Ann and Jane Taylor, both writing during the moral tale period, were sisters, but they had a sense of humor and their work had a freshness that was appealing. There was nothing priggish about their verses for children. "Twinkle, twinkle, little star" came from them. Mahlon Day also printed the work of Priscella Wakefield, and other publishers in cities along the coast of America brought out the writings of Mary M. Sherwood. Both of these English ladies were of the moral school. Priscella Wakefield was a Friend who wrote a dozen or more children's books, on historical subjects, between 1795 and 1820. Mary M. Sherwood, spent a large part of her life in trying to spread Christianity into dark places, especially India, where she lived with her husband, an army captain. Various tracts for children appeared from her pen from 1809 to 1825 or thereabouts. Mrs. Sherwood thought that all children were evil by nature and that it was the duty of parents to force them into paths of righteousness.

The writings of Mary Belson Elliott sometimes found their way into American children's chapbooks. She lived in England and her activity covered a period from about 1812 to 1860. She not only wrote pleasant things for children, but was the author of works designed to teach children. Some of her stories ran into many editions and four New York publishers reprinted some of her work.

Another author, familiar to chapbook readers, was James Hogg, the Ettrick shepherd, born in 1777 in the Vale of Ettrick. Hogg was a domestic servant, and then a shepherd. He read ceaselessly and wrote for thirty years. Scott hired him to collect old ballads for the "Border Minstrelsy." One of his pieces, in particular that appeared over and over in chapbooks, was "The Long Pack, a Northumberland Tale an hundred years old." This is blood-curdling in part and frequently causes cold shivers when read for the first time.

One could continue to mention other authors whose writings were appropriated by chapbook publishers, with and without credit. The work of Oliver Goldsmith was used sometimes, and some of Benjamin Franklin's writings proved to be unusually popular in chapbook style. Some of the poetry of Robert Burns had a chapbook all to itself, and Allan Ramsay's verses and pieces were quite popular with chapbook readers.

Chapter 4

SOME CHAPBOOK PRINTERS

It should be made apparent at the beginning of this account that the word "some" in the chapter heading is used advisedly. Perhaps it should have been replaced by "a few." There were hundreds of chapbook printers scattered all over the world and the present chapter deals only with some of the English and Scottish printers including the more important ones, whose names will always be associated with the publication of chapbooks. No personal credit is claimed for assembling this information, which is mainly the result of research work by investigators whose accomplishments are recorded in the bibliography.

Banbury, Oxfordshire, was one of the provincial towns noted for its output of chapbooks, broadsides and children's books, and in 1767 John Cheney (1732/3-1808), inn-keeper of the Unicorn at Banbury, set up a printing press and for several years he printed bill heads and sold beer. In 1771 he got into difficulties with the authorities for not having served a legal apprenticeship and he finally had to apprentice himself to a journeyman printer to keep on with his printing. He continued as a hotel keeper and printer until 1788, when during that year he gave up the hotel and moved to a new place. A poster bearing the date June 12, 1788 refers to him as "Printer, Book-Seller and Stationer, Removed from the Unicorn, to the upper End of Red-Lion Street."

John Cheney's death occurred in 1808 and his second surviving son Thomas (1782-1820) managed the press. When Thomas died the business was run by his wife Esther (1782-1859), and the firm is still in existence. However, with the advent of Esther, the publication of broadsides and chapbooks died out.

The Cheneys did general printing as well as publishing and dealing in popular literature and an inventory of the "Collections, Histories, Patters, Children's Books and Old Sheets" in stock drawn up during the period 1808 to 1820, includes 75 titles, although it is not supposed that all were printed by the Cheneys as they also sold the work of other printers. In addition to broadsides small books were printed during the last period of John Cheney's life (1788-1808). These range from 8 to 24 pages and are illustrated by woodcuts. They carry the imprint, "Cheney, Printer, Banbury." Other broadsides and chapbooks issued by the press include such titles as "The Adventures of Sir Richard Whittington," "The Bristol Garland," "A Dialogue between Honest John and Loving Kate," "The Fortune Tellers Conjuring cap," "The History of the Sleeping Beauty in the Wood," "Innocence Betrayed, or the Perjured Lover," "Mother Bunch's Closet newly broke open," etc.

During the period that Esther Cheney was running the business, another printer came on the scene in Banbury and devoted himself to publishing small chapbooks for chil- dren and other children's books, and he was a stationer and bookseller as well. This was John Golby Rusher who carried on his business from 1808 to 1877. Rusher's name is well known to persons interested in chapbooks and children's books, and his press turned out numerous horn books, primers, A B C books, toy books and battledores. Rusher was inventive and adapted various tales to his locality and the work of such artists as George Cruikshank, John and Thomas Bewick and others appears in his productions. Pear- son's "Banbury Chap Books" (London, 1890) is full of illustrations used in Banbury toy books.

In Cheap Street, Bath, Samuel Hazard conducted his printing establishment and mention has been made of his connection with the first issues of The Cheap Repository Tracts. Mr. Hazard died in September, 1806, and was greatly missed by a large circle of friends. One of the books he printed as early as 1774 is Anstey's "The Priest Dissected." Hazard was one of the best provincial printers of his day. The religious tracts, of course, were printed on poor paper, and in poor type.

Another Bath printer whose name frequently appeared on "The Cheap Repository Tracts," was John Binns, who married Hazard's daughter and became Hazard's partner. After Hazard's death, Binns continued the business until his death about 1823. His widow carried on the business until about 1856 or 1857, when G. T. Goodwin, who had married their daughter and had been in partnership for some time, appears as the sole proprietor.

Still another Bath printer, (and I should mention here, that I am indebted to Miss Elsie A. Russ for the notes about Bath printers) was Charles Ady of No. 2 Union-Passage. Some of his productions were "The Life and Adventures of Robinson Crusoe," "The Children in the Wood," and "Whittington and his Cat," and the first mentioned is dated 1813.

In the Birmingham reference library, there are chapbooks printed or published in Birmingham which bear the names of the following printers: Swinney & Hawkins, 1799; H. Butler, 1749; T. Holliwell & J. Berry, 1769; E. Jones, [c. 1790]; E. Butler, [c. 1710]; and J. Belcher & Son, T. Wood, T. Brandard, J. Russell, D. Wrighton, Swinney & Ferral, J. Hawkins, T. Bloomer, S. & T. Martin, [c. 1805 to 1825]. Some of the titles of works printed by these men are, "Cock Robin," "Cries of London," "Robin Hood," "Little Red Riding Hood," "Shepherdess of the Alps," "Jane Shore," "Thomas Hickathrift," "History of Dr. Faustus," "Ali Baba," "Judas Iscariot," "Diamonds & Toads," etc.

It is also known that a Thomas Chapman started in business in Birmingham in 1774 and supplied chapbooks, carols, songs and other sheets of the cheapest kind to street hawkers.

From about 1790 to 1840, the citizens of Coventry were able to enjoy, if they were of a mind to, from a press right in their home town, the diverting tales of Valentine and his wild brother Orson, of big-boned Mother Shipton and her prophecies, of the noble and exciting exploits of Jack the giant killer, of King Henry's experiences with the merry cobbler, of Simple Simon and his cruel wife and his misfortunes, and of the adventures of Aurelius, the London apprentice who was repulsed by his employer's daughter, the beautiful Dorinda, but who eventually vanquished two lions and married the daughter of the emperor of Turkey.

If they were not in the mood to be diverted, they could read from the same press such accounts as the history of Joseph and his brothers, or the history of Jerusalem. If they wanted witchcraft, there was the history of the Lancashire witches. And if they did not care for such long accounts as appeared in the chapbooks, they could purchase numerous and varied broadsides, on the bride's burial, the cruel step-mother, the faithless captain, the life and death of fair Rosamond, the gallant lady's fall, St. George and the dragon, etc., etc., etc.

All this was made possible by John Turner, who supplied "shopkeepers and travellers with all sorts of histories, new and old ballads, Godly and other patters, carols, Cock Robin, Tom Thumb, London cries, and various other play books for children on reasonable terms." Of course, John Turner was not the only chapbook publisher in Coventry at that time, but from the productions, now extant, from his press, he was probably the most important. Many of his broadsides and chapbooks were illustrated with the crude, and now quaint, woodcuts in use at the time. Mr. Turner, according to the advertisements in some of his chapbooks, was at one time located in High Street, Coventry, and in addition to what has been enumerated, he also sold "slip songs," valentines and valentine writers. Also many electioneering "squibs" came from his press.

Little of a biographical character is on record about John Turner. He was born about 1773, during which year there was published in Coventry a work on "The Duty of Keeping and the sin of profaning the Sabbath-Day, briefly explained," by James Turner, who may have been the father of John Turner.

Following John Turner's death in Coventry on March 18, 1863, there appeared in "The Coventry Herald" and "Observer" of March 27, 1863, the following notice:

"We last week recorded the death of John Turner, Gent. of this City, at the advanced age of 90, who formerly for many years was a respectable printer and bookseller on the premises now occupied by Mr. Tomkinson, and his eldest son was for several years proprietor of this journal. The deceased was a warm adherent of the Liberal Party, which he consistently supported through a long series of years. In 1837 he was returned to the City Council for Cross Cheaping Ward. Mr. Turner was for many years before his death entitled to the Seniority allowance as a Freeman, but gave up his claim in favour of his poorer brethren."

The Gulson (Central) Library of the City of Coventry has a good collection of Turner's chapbooks and broadsides and some of these formed part of an exhibition held, at the library in June, 1934, on the work of the early printers of Coventry. The library of Harvard University has thirty-some broadsides from Turner's press. None of these broadsides is dated, and I have never seen a date on his chapbooks.

The following short-title list of some of his broadsides represents those in Harvard University, and the chapbooks listed are, for the most part, in my possession. Perhaps someday we may have a more complete list from the Gulson Library.

To the Librarian of the City of Coventry, Mr. E. Austin Hinton, I am greatly indebted for the biographical material about John Turner, and for his informative replies to my inquiries.

BROADSIDES

The Berkshire tragedy.
The bride's burial.
The Bunter's wedding.
Catskin.
The cruel step mother.
Death and the lady.
The doating mother's garland.
The Dorsetshire garland.
Edwin and Angelina.
Exeter garland.
The faithless captain.
The famous flower of serving men.
Fisherman's garland.
The four Indian kings.
The gallant lady's fall.

The green coat boy's garland.
The life and death of fair Rosamond.
The London damsel.
The merchant's son and the beggar-wench.
No joke like a true joke.
The northern lord.
The Oxfordshire tragedy.
The Plymouth tragedy.
The politick maid of Suffolk.
St. George & the dragon.
The Turkey factor.
The unhappy lady of Hackney.
The wandering shepherdess.
William and Margaret.
The Yarmouth tragedy.

CHAPBOOKS

The complete valentine writer.
The golden chain of four links.
A groatsworth of wit for a penny.
The history of crazy Jane.
The history of Fortunatus.
The history of Jack   the giants.
The history of Jerusalem.
The history of Joseph and his
   brethren.
The history of the king and the
   cobbler.

The history of the Lancashire witches.
The history of the London 'prentice.
The history of Mother Shipton.
The history of Valentine & Orson.
The life and death of Jane Shore.
The misfortunes of Simple Simon.
Partridge and Flamstead's fortune
   book.

In Carlisle, chapbooks were printed by F. Jolie, and by F. Jolie and Sons. One, bearing the date 1770, entitled "A True and Faithful Account of the Manner of Christ's coming to Judgment on the Last Day" has been assigned to the press of Francis Jolie, who in 1794 printed and published a two volume "History of Cumberland." And later, in 1798 he issued the first number of the "Carlisle Journal." He had three sons and these in 1819, succeeded their father in continuing the newspaper. Other Carlisle chapbook printers were W. Hodgson, B. Scott and R. Johnson. B. Scott was in business in 1804, and R. Johnson in 1818.

In Kendal, Michael and Richard Branthwaite were operating as printers and book-sellers in 1803. "The Beauties of Aesop, and other Fabulists" third edition, with a frontispiece and twelve cuts by Thomas Bewick, came from their press. They printed battledores, catechisms, street songs, Watt's hymns and chapbooks and did a large whole-sale business. After the death of Michael, the business was continued for about five years by Richard and then Edward, his son, succeeded him. About 1855 the business was sold to James Robinson, who in turn sold it in 1872 to W. F. Robson, who finally became bankrupt.

During the last quarter of the eighteenth century the hawkers and peddlers of Manchester and vicinity no doubt purchased their supplies of ballads, Christmas carols, penny histories, etc., from Mr. George Swindells, a native of Disley, in Cheshire, who had his printing shop in Hanging Bridge, Manchester. He was one of the early printers of that town and upon his death on March 1, 1796, at the age of 36 years, the business was continued by A. Swindells and his eldest son John. The latter died March 13, 1853 at the age of 67.

Numerous were the songsters and chapbooks that poured from the Swindell's presses. Various garlands of choice songs, Eugene Aram, honest John and loving Kate, Tom Hickathrift, Robin Hood, Dick Turpin, Valentine and Orson, Crazy Jane, Simple Simon, Blue Beard, Robert Nixon, Jack the Giant Killer, Jane Shore, the shepherd of Salisbury Plain, Joe Miller, Mother Bunch, Doctor Faustus, the Merry Piper, Tom Thumb, the Sleep-ing Beauty and many others all issued forth to be carried in chapman's packs to the surrounding countryside where they fell into the hands of people who read them to tat-ters.

There were other chapbook printers in Manchester during the reign of the Swin-dells, but from all available information, their productions were few in number. J. Aston in 1808 published "The Ancient Ballad of Tarquin," and James Bradshaw in 1827 brought out "A Brief Sketch of the Life and Sufferings of Alice Henderson." A. Heywood appears on several, without dates.

John White, the eldest son of John White the royal printer for the city of York and the five northern counties, came to Newcastle about 1708 and set up a printing press in the Close and in 1711 started a newspaper called the "Newcastle Courant." In 1712 he moved to a new location in Newcastle called the "House on the Side," and there he developed a special line in broadsides, booklets, sermons, histories, etc., and notified chapmen that he had them for sale. His undated broadsides include "The Covetous Old Mother," "Crafty Kate of Colchester," "The Forlorn Lover," "A Lesson for All True Chris-tians," "The Careful Wife's Good Counsel," "The Kind Hearted Damsel," "The Hunting of the Hare," etc. John White also printed more important works than chapbooks and after being in business for fifty years, he had a reputation throughout the kingdom for high class work. He died at the age of eighty. When he came to Newcastle from York, he brought with him a lot of woodcuts that had belonged to his father, including some cut for Wynken de Worde, Pynson, and others down to Thomas Gent. Six years before his death in 1769 he entered into a partnership with Thomas Saint, who succeeded to White's business as printer, publisher and bookseller.

The names M. Angus and M. Angus and Son sometimes appear on Newcastle chapbooks and it is known that Thomas Angus was in business as a printer from 1774 to 1787 and Margaret Angus from 1787 to 1812. Thomas Angus in addition to other books printed the first local directory of Newcastle. In the "Newcastle Chronicle" for December 3, 1808, M. Angus and Son, "Printers, Booksellers, Bookbinders and Stationers" announced the death of a son Thomas, and the fact that another son George, had been taken into the partnership. This lasted until 1812, when M. Angus retired, leaving the business to her son George. M. Angus died December 5, 1821. The founder of the firm, Thomas Angus, died in 1788 and Margaret Angus was his widow.

W. Fordyce of 48 Dean Street, Newcastle, printed and sold a great variety of histories, ballads, songs and tales, and also school books and stationery, and W. & T. Fordyce of 15 Grey Street, Newcastle, also printed and sold chapbooks, and at one time they were located at 48 Dean Street. In fact, there are many chapbooks bearing the imprint of W. & T. Fordyce.

I am indebted for the following notes on the Fordyce family to Mr. John Oxberry of Gateshead. The firm is supposed to have had its beginning about 1825. In 1832 "A History of Tynemouth" by W. Fordyce was published. On March 12, 1834, Mary, aged 21, wife of William Fordyce, printer, died. In 1838 Richardson's "Directory of Newcastle" was printed by William and Thomas Fordyce, "printers, booksellers and agents to the Yorkshire Insurance Co., 48 Dean Street."

Shortly after the completion and publication of William Fordyce's "History of Durham," in 1857, it is supposed that he died, but on the other hand the name of William Fordyce appears in "Ward's Directory of Newcastle" for 1863, as "publisher, 10 New Bridge Street." Thomas Fordyce continued in business at 60 Dean Street for many years and died June 30, 1889, at the age of 79. It is recorded that William Fordyce was second only to John Marshall in the production of chapbooks.

John Marshall had a place in the Old Flesh Market, Newcastle upon Tyne, where he printed garlands and chapbooks and sold a large assortment of songs, ballads, tales and histories. It is supposed that he was in business in Newcastle around the year 1820.

In Northampton chapbooks were printed by C. Dicey, Robert Dicey, W. Dicey, Wm. Dicey, William Dicey, W. & C. Dicey, William and Cluer Dicey and R. Raikes and C. Dicey, so the imprints run. The first printing press in Northampton was set up by the Diceys and they were the most noted of local printers. W. Dicey and R. Raikes printed "The St. Ives Mercury," and a little later, or in 1720, this was followed by the establishment of another newspaper, "The Northampton Mercury," which was printed in George Row until 1730, when he opened an office on the Parade. The May 2, 1885 issue of "The Northampton Mercury," was the last number they issued, thus establishing a record of 165 years during which this paper carried the Dicey imprint. The paper was sold to S. S. Campion. Robert Raikes, who was associated at different times with W. Dicey, was the father of the founder of various Sunday schools. Robert Raikes and W. Dicey, on the last day of January, 1720-1, printed the first number of "The Northampton Miscellany," a crown octavo monthly periodical which did not extend beyond six numbers. As early as 1725, W. Dicey printed a chapbook, "The Life of Jonathon Wilde," (sic.) in Northampton that sold for 4 d. This is located in the British Museum. Various chapbooks and broadsides were printed by William Dicey who advertised, "All Sorts of Old and New Ballads, Broad Sheets, Histories, Copper Plates, Pictures cut in Wood, &c., much better printed, and cheaper than at any other Place in England."

Large numbers of chapbooks bearing the imprint "Printed and Sold in Aldemary Churchyard, London," were issued by the Diceys, but seldom bear their name, and it is the belief of Mr. Stewart Beattie that the majority of them were printed in Northampton and sent to London. A 24-page chapbook on "The Conquest of France" bears the following imprint, "London, C. Dicey, in Bow Church Yard; sold also at his warehouse in Northampton." It is supposed that the Dicey place of business was moved from Aldemary Churchyard to Bow Church Yard, from which most of the London Dicey Chapbooks were issued. Other chapbooks were issued by William Dicey and Company, in Bow Churchyard, by Cluer Dicey in Bow Church Yard, by Dicey and Co., in Aldermary Church Yard, and By W. and C. Dicey in Bow Church Yard.

Upon Penrith chapbooks we find the names of Ann Bell, A. Bell, Anthony Soulby, A. Soulby, F. Jollie, Junr., and J. Allison. According to the Penrith "Registers," a widow, aged 98, probably the printer's mother, was buried in 1799. On March 31, 1800, Ann, daughter of William Bell and Mary, his wife, was baptised. On May 15, 1804, Ann, daughter of John Bell and Mary, his wife, was baptised. In May, 1820, there was another baptism, this time of Mary, daughter of Joseph and Ann Bell; and in August of the same year, Ann, daughter of Edward and Mary Bell was baptised. In November, 1821, Joseph and Ann Bell had their daughter Jane baptised; and on December 8, 1823, Ann Bell, widow, aged 73, was buried. Lastly, on April 24, 1825, Joseph and Ann Bell had another daughter, Elizabeth, baptised. From these facts, collectors of chapbooks having Ann Bell imprints are invited to draw their own conclusions relative to the dates of issuance.

Relative to Anthony Souby, on May 11, 1790, William, the son of Anthony and Nanny Soulby, was baptised, and the next year, in September, he was buried. On January 18, 1792, Dorothy Soulby, aged 13, was buried, and on April 13, 1807, Margaret Soulby, aged 63, was buried, as was Barbara, aged 16, daughter of Anthony and Ann Soulby in 1803. Anthony Soulby was a churchwarden in 1801. He purchased many cuts from the Bewicks and many of his songsters carried Bewick wood blocks.

Allison was printing in 1836 at which time he published a guide to Penrith. He failed in 1841 and his business was continued by B. T. Sweeten.

In Whitehaven, "The Constant Lovers Garland," "The Merry and Entertaining Jokes of George Buchanan," "The History of the King and the Cobler," "The Danger of Evil Company," and many of their relatives were printed by A. Coutts, J. Dunn, Ann Dunn, B. N. Dunn, J. Briscoe, T. Wilson, T. Nicholson, and perhaps others. According to Ferguson, to whose writings I am indebted for these and other notes, Alexander Coutts had his house and office in the Market Place, like other Whitehaven printers. In addition to chapbooks, Coutts started the "Cumberland Chronicle" in 1776, which ceased publication in 1799. Mr. Coutts death occurred in March, 1795.

John Dunn had his shop in an old, white house in Whitehaven and was "famed for his powdered pigtail, his wooden leg, and his manufacture of red ink." He was engaged in various types of business. In 1776, the office of the "Cumberland Register," was kept in Dunn's Shop, by Skleton and Co., and apparently Dunn was in some sort of partnership with Skelton, because after two years, they had a falling out and in the "Pacquet" Skelton warned those indebted to them not to pay any money to J. Dunn, one reason being that he was an officer in the Customs. In 1777 an amusing notice appeared in the "Pacquet," telling the public not to care whether or not John Dunn paid 13 pounds for his recipe and to be sure to ask for "Briscoe's Panacea." Joseph Briscoe was a rival printer and at that time many printers sold patent medicines. In January, 1778, a notice appeared in the "Pacquet" to the effect that John Dunn, "formerly a bookseller in this town," had taken the sacrament at Church previous to taking the oath as deputy Searcher at the port of Whitehaven. Browning N. Dunn and A. Dunn, were probably relatives of John Dunn who carried on the printing business after he was made an officer in the Customs.

Joseph Briscoe printed the "Cumberland Magazine, or Whitehaven Monthly Miscellany," which ran from 1778 to 1780 and perhaps later. In April, 1783, an announcement in the "Pacquet" stated that he was leaving Whitehaven, in favor of his brother Francis, for a printing office and stationery warehouse at the Isle of Man. Apparently Francis Briscoe did not print many chapbooks, but Ferguson records a 64-page one, printed by Briscoe on "The Surprising Adventures of John Roach, Mariner of Whitehaven," etc., and it turns out that Roach really was a Whitehaven sailor who had arrived after an absence of fifteen years, during which time he had had adventures among the Mexican Indians and Spaniards.

Thomas Wilson printed playbills, songs, plays, placards, etc., as well as chapbooks, and he was also a bookseller and stationer. He was the accepted printer for the theatrical profession and the theatre box plan was kept in his shop at the corner of

Lowther Street and King Street. Mr. Wilson died in 1851 or 1852. He had a son, William Wilson, who followed along after his father in the same lines of printing.

Thomas Nicholson was in business in Roper Street where he specialized in play-bills and songs. He was apparently still alive and living at Leeds in 1894.

Mention has been made of Thomas Gent and of John White, the royal printer for the city of York, and of the importance of York in the chapbook trade. There were other printers there too, such as C. Croshaw of Coppergate (c. 1820), Thomas Wilson and Son (1811), Peter Brown, Carrall, T. Wilson and R. Spence (1803), but the most active in producing songs, pamphlets and toy chapbooks for children was James Kendrew, who start-ed about 1803. The woodcuts for many of Kendrew's books were made in York by a man named Carrall and the valentines and plates for chapbooks were colored by hand by Ken-drew's daughter and other young female relatives in their leisure hours away from school. In 1841 James Kendrew was succeeded by his son John L. Kendrew, but in 1848 John sold the plant to someone in York. His nephew James H. Carr entered the business in 1869 and took it over after the death of his uncle in 1874. The British Museum has a large number of Kendrew publications, which cover the entire range of chapbook litera-ture, including his cataogues and circulars to customers.

About London it is practically impossible to put down any consistent and in-formative account of the chapbook printers of the eighteenth century. They and their productions were so numerous that it would require years of effort to assemble something of their lives and, even then, the record would not be complete. However, some of the most active ones in the chapbook field may be mentioned, together with approximate dates indicating some of the periods in which they were in business.

In the "Catalogue of a Collection of English Ballads of the xviith and xviiith Centuries," privately printed in 1890 (Bibliotheca Lindesiana), there is an extensive list of London printers, publishers and booksellers, but as most of these printed and sold, for the most part, black letter ballads, we need not be particularly concerned with them here. Nevertheless, the list with its accompanying dates is useful to collec-tors who may be interested in knowing when some of their broadsides were published.

In the "Catalogue of English and American Chap-Books and Broadside Ballads in Harvard College Library" there are over 250 London printers, publishers, and booksellers mentioned as individuals or firms in the index, and in the "Catalogue of the chapbooks in the New York Public Library" there are 76 London printers listed. Some of these chapbook producers were in business only a short time. Others continued for a long time. They moved from one location to another, entered into partnerships that in many cases did not last, had their own names put on chapbooks printed by others, and all in all there is a nice state of confusion waiting for someone to untangle.

As early as 1608 "The Seven Champions of Christendom" was licensed to be print-ed in London and editions were published in 1616, 1675, 1676, 1680, 1686, 1687, 1696 and 1705. "Guy of Warwick" was licensed in 1640 and also appeared in 1685, 1695 and 1703. Such chapbooks circulated along with the more numerous black letter ballads and were brought out by such firms as Andrew Crook, and W. Thackeray who was "at the Golden Sugar Loaf, near the Crown Tavern in Duck Lane" from about 1660 to 1680, and "at the Angel in Duck Lane" from about 1680 to 1693.

Reference has been made to the Diceys of Northampton and of their location in London. It is thought by some that William Dicey moved from Northampton to Bow Church-yard about 1730. John Cluer, who later established a reputation as a music publisher, first started in Bow Churchyard and printed ballads. This was about 1700 to 1710. Wil-liam Dicey was supposed to have followed him in this line. As late as 1763, Dicey & Okell were advertising the sale of patent medicines, mainly in provincial newspapers.

An interesting catalogue of 120 pages was issued by Cluer Dicey and Richard Marshall in 1764 from their printing office in Aldemary Churchyard, London. It con-tains a list of over 1,000 engravings of portraits, maps, views, scriptural and emblematic pictures and lists of 150 titles of histories, many of which are familiar to chapbook collectors. It also includes lists of old ballads, carols, song collections, patters, etc. Old ballads, collections of songs and 8-page patters were priced "48 to the Quire, and 20 Quires to the Ream, per Ream 4 shillings." Other prices were quoted as follows: "Penny History Books, 104 at 2 s., 6 d; Small Histories or Books of Amusement for Children, on various subjects, adorned with a variety of Cuts, 100 at 6 s., ditto stich'd on embossed paper, 13 for 9 d."

A name long associated with publishing in London is Marshall. At the Bible in Newgate Street, from about 1679 to about 1725 Joseph and William Marshall conducted their business. In 1793-4 John Marshall issued engraved song-sheets and chapbooks from his place in Aldermary Church Yard but he later, about 1799, moved to a place in Cheapside. There was also a John Marshall of Gracechurch Street, who advertised chapmen's books, broadsides, lottery pictures, London "crys" by the gross or dozen, also labels for "Chryrurgeons Chests," funeral tickets and "affidavits for burials in woollen," etc. Darton states that John Marshall of 4 Aldermary Church Yard was in business as early as 1783 and about 1799 he had a place at 17 Queen Street, Cheapside, and in 1800 another at 140 Fleet Street where he or a firm of the same name remained until at least 1813; however, this John Marshall published nothing but children's books of good quality. On the other hand, issues of chapbooks by the Marshalls, with the imprint "Aldermary Church Yard" are extant in numbers and must originally have been issued in extensive quantities.

For over 150 years, the Dartons have been connected with publishing in London. William Darton, Senior, started in business in 1785 as engraver, printer, binder and publisher, on Gracechurch Street. Although noted for their children's books, and for certain writers whom they introduced to English children, once in a while a few of their publications manage to get listed as chapbooks. Those interested in the Darton firms and their imprints from 1785 to 1866 will find an interesting table included in "The Juvenilia of Mary Belson Elliott," published by the New York Public Library in 1936.

About the beginning of the 19th century J. Pitts appeared at No. 6 Great Andrew Street and was the leader in the Seven Dials district for the printing of ballads, garlands and other street literature, and in addition, J. Pitts sold toys, marbles and other playthings for children. Charles Hindley in "The History of the Catnach Press" (London 1886) states that "Johnny" Pitts was a woman, a coarse female who had originally followed the trade of bumboat woman at Portsmouth and that for a time intense rivalry existed between her and "Jemmy" Catnach. It is said that Pitts disappeared from the chapbook world about 1815.

Mr. Plummer of Seething Lane printed many of Thomas Tegg's chapbooks relating to the sea. These usually had engraved, folding frontispieces and such long descriptive titles that it would seem to be unnecessary to read the account. Tegg's titles of this sort included the "Affecting narrative of the loss of the Grosvener," "Affecting narrative of the loss of the Thames Smack, Captain Craiggy," "Correct statement of the loss of the Earl of Abergavenny," "The destruction of the Boyne," "Struggles of Capt. Thomas Keith in America." These, of course, are short titles. The complete titles told of "unparalleled sufferings," and "wonderful deliverance," "miraculous preservation" and the "cruelty of pirates."

Thomas Tegg was born at Wimbledon in Surrey, March 4, 1776. He was apprenticed to a bookseller at Dalkeith and eventually became one of the chief booksellers of London. He ran away from his intolerable master Alexander Meggett and tried to make a living selling chapbooks. Finally he made his way to London and in 1796 got a job in Lane's "Minerva Library" in Leadenhall Street. Here he was discharged for telling a truth that placed his employer in a bad light and eventually, with a small sum of money, he became the partner of a book dealer in Aldersgate Street. After various other bookish employments, including that of auctioneer, Tegg gradually made his way as a publisher and his earliest productions were pamphlets containing abridged accounts of popular works, embellished with frontispieces. He purchased "remainders" for resale and his reputation rests mainly upon his cheap reprints and curtailed accounts of popular works. He died April 21, 1845, and was succeeded in London by his son and late partner William Tegg.

Other printers and publishers of chapbooks in London were Dean & Munday, Thos. Dean & Son, and Dean & Bailey, who probably were in business from about 1800 to 1830; T. and R. Hughes, 35 Ludgate Street, around 1808; Tabard & Co., 157 New Bond Street about 1807; J. Evans and Son, Long-Lane, about 1820; John Evans of 42 Long-Lane, who printed ballads in 1791 and no doubt before that date; J. Davenport and C. Sheppard, around 1797; Orlando Hodgson, 5 Cloth Fair, West Smithfield, 1830-35; J. L. Marks, 23 Russel Court, Covent Garden, around 1821; and one could continue this list for many pages.

It is appropriate to close this account with the picturesque and prolific chapbook firm known as "The Catnach Press" of Seven Dials, London. Mr. Charles Hindley's able and interesting book "The History of the Catnach Press" which was published in London in 1886 is the standard work on this press and everyone writing about the Catnachs is indebted to Mr. Hindley.

There were two Catnachs which concern us here, John Catnach, the father, and James, one of the sons, more popularly called "Jemmy," later "Old Jemmy." John was born in 1769 at Burntisland, Fifeshire, Scotland. His family moved to Edinburgh and John was bound out to a printer. After serving his apprenticeship he worked in Edinburgh as a journeyman printer and then started his own business in Berwick-upon-Tweed where he married. In 1790 he moved his business to Alnwick, England, where he printed worth-while books that were illustrated by Thomas Bewick and Luke Clennell, and also a series of juvenile works such as "The Royal Play Book," "The Death and Burial of Cock Robin," etc., which were also illustrated by Thomas Bewick's cuts.

In 1807 he entered into a partnership with Mr. William Davison, a chemist, and there were books published bearing the imprint of the firm of Catnach and Davison. This partnership did not last long and in 1808 Mr. Davison was issuing books under his own imprint, later including a series of halfpenny books illustrated by some of Thomas Bewick's finest engravings.

Toward the end of 1808 John Catnach and his family moved to Newcastle-upon-Tyne, where he set up his press and managed to get into debt and also into the debtor's prison, not, however, before he managed to send his wife and daughters to London, together with a wooden printing press and a few other articles of his trade. Upon his release from prison he joined them, but never succeeded in getting ahead. In the absence of high-class work he had to print quarter-sheet ballads. At this time he was located at 60 Wardour Street, Soho-Square. In August, 1813, he injured his leg through a fall and died on December 4 of the same year.

His son James, born in 1792, who had learned his trade under his father, took over the business and moved to Seven Dials, where he had difficulty at first in view of the competition from "Johnny" Pitts' press. They printed virulent lampoons against each other and called each other names in print. However, Catnach worked hard and lived hard and turned out such penny histories, street-papers, and halfpenny songs as he could. In 1818 he ran afoul of the libel laws and spent six months in the House of Correction at Clerkenwell. During this time his mother and sisters, with whom he had lived, carried on the business of writing and printing the squibs and street ballads.

In 1820 his business took an upturn. Certain public happenings enabled the Street Literature printers to produce "Full Particulars" for street sale and Catnach came in for a fair share of the work, and he too was engaged in getting out lampoons and songs. With a larger income, he increased the capacity of his plant and after a short time he too was engaged in literary piracy, along with his colleagues. And soon the Catnach Press was turning out news of duels, scandals, assassinations, sudden deaths of prominent persons, elopements, public executions, last words of criminals, murders,

etc., which people still like to read about. All of which added to his income and made
him important as the high priest of street literature, even though his productions were
a sorry looking lot with their ghastly woodcut illustrations and terrible printing due
to his haphazard use of old blocks and founts of type which he bought up at auction
sales.

However, James Catnach also turned out, much better than did his rivals, large
quantities of children's farthing, halfpenny and penny books, which are now eagerly
sought for by collectors. These juvenile chapbooks printed by James Catnach of Monmouth
Court, Seven Dials, were always well illustrated, sometimes colored, and had colored
paper covers. "Jerry Diddle and his Fiddle," "Jumping Joan," "The Butterfly's Ball,"
"Old Mother Hubbard and her Wonderful Dog," "Little Red Riding Hood," "Cinderella," "The
Life and Adventures of Dick Turpin," "The Liverpool Tragedy," and many other titles, as
well as primers, battledores, catchpennies, songs, colored penny books, ballads, poetry
cards, hymns, valentines, Christmas pieces, lotteries, sheet almanacs, etc., poured from
The Catnach Press by the thousands, and supplied country shops, chapmen, and hawkers.
At times James Catnach was his own engraver, and one block was frequently put to many
uses. Everything was adorned or illustrated regardless of the fitness of the illustration. However, the illustrations in his children's books were inserted with more care
and as a rule, fitted in with the text.

James Catnach retired in 1838, and left his business to Mrs. Annie Ryle, his
sister. He died a bachelor, on February 1, 1841. After Catnach's death, James Paul,
who had worked for Mr. Catnach from boyhood on, entered into a partnership with Mrs.
Ryle. In 1845 this was dissolved and the business was carried on as Ryle & Co., ultimately becoming the property, in 1856, of Mr. W. S. Fortey, whose imprint continued to
appear on productions that were still characteristic of the Catnach Press, and who remained in Monmouth Court until modern improvements swept it away.

Mention has been made of some of the towns in Scotland in which chapbooks were
printed, and of Dougal Graham's place in chapbook history. In addition to poems,
sketches and songs native to Scotland, the chapbook literature of this country included
many accounts of English authorship. They were turned out by Scottish presses and
hawked about at fairs and markets all over Scotland. It is difficult to write more than
a fragmentary account of these presses that printed so many wares for the Flying Stationers. At one time Dr. Robert Chambers estimated the annual circulation of chapbooks
in Scotland to be 200,000, which seems to be a modest figure.

Mr. John A. Fairley, in his article on "Chapbooks and Aberdeen Chapbooks" (1916),
lists a number of Aberdeen chapbooks that were once in his possession. Undated ones
carry the imprints of J. Chalmers & Co., Castlestreet, Aberdeen, A. Kieth, Long Acre,
and W. Gordon, Upperkirkgate, Aberdeen, and Lewis Smith & Son, Aberdeen. The dated ones,
all from Aberdeen, have the following imprints: A. Imlay, No. 3 George Street, 1801;
George Clark And Son, 17 Broad Street, 1868; James Clark, 17 Broad Street, 1869; Lewis
Smith & Son, 1888, and 1893. Chapbooks as late as 1893!

In Aberdeen, 1915, there was published under the authorship of William Walker,
"Peter Buchan and Other Papers on Scottish and English Ballads and Songs." This contains the life of Buchan and a bibliography of his works, including thirty-two chapbooks
that he published at Peterhead from 1817 to 1824. Many pages are devoted to defending
the authenticity of Scottish claims to certain songs, and the Motherwell collection of
chapbooks is described.

Previous to Walker's book, Mr. James Cameron wrote a "Bibliography of the Publications of Peter Buchan of Peterhead" that appeared in the transactions of the Edinburgh
Bibliographical Society, vol. 4, p. 105-116, 1900. In this paper Cameron lists the
titles of 36 works, mostly by Buchan and mostly from his press. In addition there are
twenty titles of chapbooks printed at Peterhead by Buchan from 1817 to 1824. These are
nearly all small octavos of eight pages, which are exceedingly scarce. They include such
titles as "The Enchanted Lover," "A Dispute between the Gardeners and the Tailors for

the Antiquity of their Trades," "Three Excellent Songs," "The Buchanshire Tragedy," "The Duke of Gordon's Three Daughters," "Captain Glen's Unhappy Voyage to New Barbary" and "A Pennyworth of Wit."

Peter Buchan was born in Peterhead in 1790. He had little schooling and lived a varied early life and he became a good student and collector of native ballads and stories, in addition to his capacities as author, editor, publisher, printer and engraver. In 1814 his first volume of verse, "The Recreation of Leisure Hours," appeared at Edinburgh. It is stated that he served only an apprenticeship of ten days in a printing office at Stirling in 1816, returning to Peterhead the same year and starting a press of his own. While at Edinburgh in 1816 he visited the Earl of Buchan and gained his friendship and patronage. From 1816 to 1828, many works were issued from his press. In 1819 he invented a press that worked with the feet instead of the hands. He ultimately left Peterhead and lived at Aberdeen, Edinburgh, Glasgow and other places. He was friendly with Sir Walter Scott, David Laing, William Motherwell, etc. His death happened suddenly at London, on September 19, 1854.

In Glasgow the firm of James & Matthew Robertson of Saltmarket printed chapbooks extensively and is supposed to have realized 30,000 pounds from their sales. Some of their work is dated from 1787 to 1807. There was also a John Robertson in 1774, and J. & J. Robertson, 1779-1782. In the same city, located also in the historic Saltmarket were Robert Hutchison, bookseller, and James Duncan, (1746), the former's publications being dated from about 1815 to 1830. In the same city there were also T. Johnson, 1812, J. Lumsden & Son, 1814-1820, and Francis Orr, who started in business about 1790. In 1825 he took his three sons into the firm and the name became Francis Orr & Sons; thousands of Glasgow chapbooks carried only the information, "Printed for the Booksellers," as late as 1850.

In Edinburgh the most active printers of chapbooks were J. Morren, (c. 1800-1820), and Alexander Robertson, and the centers of publication were Niddery's Wynd (1775-1780) and Cowgate. Other publishers were D. Webster and Son, and William Cameron, both about 1820.

In Falkirk, T. Johnston was an outstanding publisher and issued many chapbooks, some of which are dated from 1798 to 1827, and in Kilmarnock, there was H. Crawford (c. 1815-1820). In Paisley we find that George Caldwell was an outstanding publisher of chapbooks and also Caldwell and Son, these firms operating in 1820 and 1839. John Neilson was once in Paisley around 1815 and 1821, but later he moved to Glasgow and opened a printing office in the Trongate. John Miller of Paisley, who operated a bookshop at Sandholes, was apparently publisher and editor of the "Paisley Repository," (c. 1810) a sort of serial chapbook that was printed at different times by Andrew Young and John Neilson. Andrew Young also moved to Glasgow at one time and had his office in the Trongate, where he did printing for religious societies. He died in 1831 and for a while the business was carried on by his son.

Stirling had four printers who turned out chapbooks, C. Randall, around 1799-1812; M. Randall, around 1814-1820; W. Macnie about 1820-1826, who printed many garlands, and J. Fraser & Co., around 1820. J. & J. Neil at Airdrie, about 1823-1825, printed many song-garlands. It should be understood that the dates following the names of printers do not represent the actual periods the firms were in existence, but represnet, for the most part, dates which appear on some of the chapbooks from their presses.

"The Millers of Haddington, Dunbar and Dunfermline," of which George Miller was once a chapbook printer, are adequately treated by W. J. Cowper in his book of that title, published in London in 1914. George Miller was born January 14, 1771, in Dunbar and was apprenticed in 1785 to Alexander Smart, a bookseller, for four years of service. Smart left for Edinburgh in 1787 and Miller went with him. He did not learn much, however, and in September, 1788, the indenture was broken with mutual consent. George then for two and a half years conducted with his brother James a combination book and gorcery store in Dunbar. The place was opened in 1789, but the partnership was dissolved in 1791 and each continued independently. In his book department George sold small histories, children's books, sermons, ballads, and pictures, and he also conducted a circulating library and wrote articles for the press.

In 1795 he bought a printing press and established the East Lothian Press, the first in East Lothian. At first he was his own compositor and pressman. By 1801 he had a second press and was printing such works as Robinson Crusoe, a duodecimo of 238 pages. At first he printed ballads, catechisms, and 24-page chapbooks including titles such as "The Life and History of the Famous Mother Shipton," (1795?), "An Account of Several Remarkable Earthquakes," (1799), "Comical Sayings of Pady from Cork," (1799?), "The World Turned Upside Down," (1800), and "The Laird of Cool's Ghost," (1799). Later, or in 1802-1804, he substituted religious and moral publications for the chapbooks, which he called Cheap Tracts. There were 20 titles in the series including "Serious Thoughts for the Living," "The Magdalen," "The Slave Trade," "Counsels to Young Men," "The Death Bed," and "The Honest Debtor." He was through with his former chapbooks and called them pernicious trash. He prospered and at the end of 1804, moved the printing part of his business to Haddington, but after a year he returned to Dunbar and left his son James in charge at Haddington. In 1815 his business was at its best and his work had expanded, but a trade depression set in, work fell off, and for several years he had a difficult time, which was finally ended by bankruptcy in 1832, when he lost even his household furniture. In addition to his articles, he wrote several broadside ballads, and other works including a "History of Dunbar," and "Tom Bragwell," designed to prevent juvenile crimes. In 1813 he also started "The Cheap Magazine or Poor Man's Fireside Companion." He died July 26, 1835.

In closing this, to me, far from satisfactory account of some of the printers, I might say that for collectors the problem of dating chapbooks is never closed. Just as soon as one is reasonably certain of the approximate dates during which a particular printer operated, along comes something, either to himself or to another collector, which makes it necessary for him to revise, or add to, his information. And it is necessary for me to leave in the mind of the reader the fact that there have been omitted the names of numerous, in fact, hundreds of printers and publishers, lest this chapter become mainly a check-list of printers, which is not my object at all.

Chapter 5

OF THE CONTENTS OF CHAPBOOKS IN GENERAL

Again I am surrounded by difficulties. The subjects of fugitive popular literature are so numerous and there are so many different versions of some subjects that it
is necessary for me to group chapbooks into several broad classes and to be specific
only about a few popular chapbooks in each class. The literature of centuries appeared,
in a curtailed and debased form, in the chapbooks that circulated over a half century,
and now even greater curtailment is necessary. However, it is hoped that the following
accounts will enable one to form an idea of the numerous and diverting things found in
chapbooks and perhaps whet one's appetite for more.

Although a subjective division is usually bibliographically bad, because of individual differences of opinion regarding the limits of such division, for the present
purpose, I think that such a division is best. And as the subject classification in the
Harvard College Library "Catalogue of English and American Chap-Books and Broadside Ballads" seems adequate for my purpose, I shall follow it, with some modifications. In
this catalogue, chapbooks are grouped into 23 general classes which I have reduced by
some combinations to the following eighteen: 1, Religious and Moral, Sunday Reading,
Cheap Repository Tracts; 2, Household Manuals, etc.; 3, Historical, Political, and Biographical; 4, Geographical Description and Local History; 5, Travel and Adventure;
6, Odd Characters and Strange Events; 7, Prose Fiction; 8, Legendary Romances, Fairy
Stories and Folk-Tales in Prose; 9, Dramatic; 10, Metrical Tales and other Verse;
11, Song Books; 12, Jest Books, Humorous Fiction, Riddles, etc.; 13, Humorous Metrical
Tales; 14, Dream Books, Fortune Telling, and Legerdemain; 15, Demonology and Witchcraft;
16, Prophecies; 17, Crime and Criminals; 18, Miscellaneous, including Social Satire,
Matrimony, Manners and Customs, Proverbs, etc.

Mention has been made of the long titles of many chapbooks, some of them being
as descriptive as a table of contents. For example, a chapbook founded on Defoe's "Moll
Flanders" published in Aldemary Church Yard, London, is entitled "The fortunes and misfortunes of Moll Flanders who was born in Newgate, and during a life of continued variety for sixty years, was 17 times a whore, 5 times a wife, whereof once to her own
brother, 12 times a thief, 11 times in Bridewell, 9 times in New-Prison, 11 times in
Woodstreet Compter, 6 times in the Poultry Compter, 14 times in the Gate-House, 25 times
in New-Gate,.....8 years a transport to Virginia. At last grew rich, lived honest, and
died penitent."

Another example of a long title is found in one printed at Petersgate in 1772,
called "The jester's gimcrack; or Two pennyworth of fun. Containing merry stories,
smart repartees, droll sayings, youthful pranks, ridiculous bulls, funny jokes, &c. of
the English, Irish, Scotch, and Welsh manufacture. To which are added a variety of
conundrums, toasts, sentiments, hob-nobs, &c. The whole adapted to the capacities of
youth as well as infants six feet high, and calculated for the entertainment of persons
of both sexes of whatever age, size, sect, or denomination. Multum in parvo. Compiled
(with additions) by John Pendred, York, printed by somebody, sold to anybody, may be
read by everybody excepting nobody, either when he is in company or when nobody's with
him but himself alone at sea."

These are not the longest ones that have come to my notice, and many are much
shorter, nevertheless they illustrate the wordiness of chapbook titles in general.

Chapter 6

OF RELIGIOUS AND MORAL CHAPBOOKS

Although religion and morals were not as popular as other subjects, nevertheless at one time there was a plentiful supply, in chapbook form of sermons, sinner's sobs, prayers, divine songs, protests against whisky, conversions of sinners and heathen, catechisms, punishments of blasphemers, dialogues between the angel of death and various persons, and of histories of Moses, Jesus, Judas Iscariot and other Biblical personages and incidents. The moral tales are best exemplified by some of the Cheap Repository tracts of Hannah More, and by temperance lectures. No subject was too large for chapbook treatment, and we find that A. Campbell wrote "The History of All Religions" in 1822 for a 24-page chapbook. This included the churches, parties and sectaries of twenty-eight different religions, including the Burghers, Antiburghers, Old Light Burghers, New Light Burghers, Pedobaptists, Bereans, Socinians and Douglasites. The pictorial Bibles and such accounts as "The Pilgrim's Progress" lent themselves readily to illustration and these were always "embellished" with numerous wood cuts, in fact they are mainly picture books with a few lines of text or verse beneath each picture. "The Wandering Jew, or the Shoemaker of Jerusalem, who lived when our Lord and Saviour Jesus Christ was crucified, and by Him appointed to wander until he comes again. With his travels, method of living and a discourse with some clergymen about the end of the world," was a favorite topic for chapbook circulation. The story is too well known for repetition.

An Aldermary Church-yard chapbook of 1785 has the following descriptive and informative title, "The Blasphemer's Punishment, or the Cries of the Son of God to the whole World, being a true and faithful account of one Elizabeth Dover, a knight and baronet's daughter, twenty-one years of age, who never would believe that there was either God or Devil, heaven or hell, or any future state after this life was ended; till last Sunday was three weeks, as she was walking in the fields with some of her wicked companions swearing. If there is a devil, let me see him, that I may know him another time."

In order to find out what happened to Elizabeth one has to read the text of this chapbook, something that is not always necessary in view of what is usually contained in the title.

J. Marshall of Newcastle printed "The Surprising Recovery of Dr. James Scott, Minister of the Gospel in the Parish of St. Clement's, Oxford, Who Preached a Sermon to his Congregation after being Three Days and Nights in a Coffin, on the 10th of November last." And the combined cover and title page is decorated with a crude woodcut of a coffin. Dr. Scott was in his coffin, without any appearance of life, in fact he was even cold, and the funeral sermon had been preached, and as the coffin was being lowered into the grave, a noise and groaning was heard. The coffin was opened and to the great astonishment of everyone, Dr. Scott sat up and faintly bade them not to be afraid. After a short stay in a warm bed Dr. Scott related his experience in having his sins exposed to him, in addition to his charitable acts by an angel who told him to return to the world with a message to the effect that the Lord's coming would be shown by certain signs from Heaven. Among these signs were earthquakes in Spain and Italy and the conversion of many Turks to the Christian faith.

"The Cries of a Wounded Conscience; Or, The Sorrowful Sighs of a Trembling Sinner at the Point of Death" is not as intriguing as one would suppose from the title. It is in verse and the sinner does not go into any detail about his wicked life, preferring to be very general about his sins.

In "The Lost and Undone Son of Perdition, or the Life and Death of Judas Iscariot," the following view is expressed:

> The love of money is a rock
> Which causes care and trouble,
> And he that hasteth to be rich,
> He makes his sorrows double.
>
> Money's a most alluring bate
> Conducive unto evil,
> For this, base Judas sold his God,
> Himself unto the devil.

Many religious chapbooks, such as "Heavenly Rest for a Weary Soul; being the Last Legacy of a Father to his Children when on his death bed," and "A Journey from Time to Eternity," and "The Repentance and Happy Death, of the Celebrated Earl of Rochester," are dull. In fact many of them are ultra-dull, and there is no point in reproducing their dullness even though they were supposed not to have been dull when they were issued and even though their original readers did not question their dullness.

The moral tales found in chapbooks are less dull, probably because many of them contain references to everyday doings of people, but a steady diet of them for several hours produces weariness. I fear that this type of Sunday reading was often forced upon young persons by their elders.

With some difficulty Mercy was admitted, and they safely arrived at Interpreter's house; supper being ready, and thanks given, they partook of a hearty repast; Interpreter asked how she became a pilgrim, she said, it was by the loss of her husband, and a letter from the King of Zion.

Figure 8

A page from a chapbook edition of
"The Pilgrim's Progress."

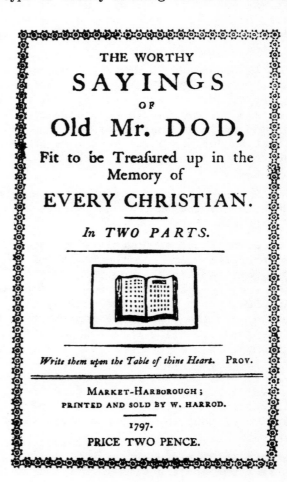

THE WORTHY
SAYINGS
OF
Old Mr. DOD,
Fit to be Treasured up in the
Memory of
EVERY CHRISTIAN.

In TWO PARTS.

Write them upon the Table of thine Heart. PROV.

MARKET-HARBOROUGH;
PRINTED AND SOLD BY W. HARROD.

1797.
PRICE TWO PENCE.

Figure 9

The Worthy Sayings of Old Mr. Dod.

According to "The Happy Man. The True Gentleman. How to Live in this Word" one of "Marshall's Religious Tracts," printed in Newcastle, the true gentleman," is God's servant, the world's master and his own conqueror; virtue is his business, study is his recreation, contentment is his rest, and happiness is his reward; God is his father, the Church is his mother, the Saints are his brethren; all that need are his friends; Heaven is his inheritance, Religion is his chaplain, Charity is his chamberlain, Sobriety is his butler, Temperance is his cook, Hospitality is his housekeeper, Providence is his house, and Discretion is his porter, to let in and out as most fit. He is the true master of the family; and all his business he is necessitated to take by the way of heaven, he keeps under his feet; and all his happiness, by the way, is to make himself and others happy."

As illustrating the reward of certain types of wickedness we have "The Remarkable Account of John Williams. Who giving his Mind up to all Manner of Wickedness, and being in the Field at Plough blaspheming the Name of his Maker; the Horses, Plough, and himself, suddenly sank into the Ground, where they now remain, except the Horses, and cannot be moved; to the great Astonishment of Thousands of Spectators, who daily resort to see them." To deserve what happened, Mr. Williams had been giving his mind to horse racing, cock fighting, card playing, wenching and drinking. Twelve clergymen attended to him during his misfortune and prayed for him amidst 5,000 spectators. They tried to feed him, with a teaspoon and a feather, but he could not open his mouth and when the earth was dug away from him by day, the work was demolished during the night. The final outcome is not mentioned in the chapbook, but the opportunity is taken to call attention to "how dreadful the torments of the damned must be, to lie howling in hell."

In "The Worthy Sayings of Old Mr. Dod, Fit to be Treasured up in the Memory of Every Christian," published in 1797, directions are given for taking stock of one's self every day, morning and night, and riotous living is deplored. However, it was Mr. Dod's belief that a man was never undone till in Hell.

A popular moral chapbook, printed many times by various firms, was "The History of Charles Jones, the footman. Shewing how he raised himself from the humble station of a foot boy, to a place of great eminence and trust, by his honesty and integrity." Needless to say, in addition, Charles Jones was extremely religious. Most of the moral and religious chapbooks are of English origin, nevertheless certain titles originating in Scotland had a wide circulation. One of these was "Scotland's Skaith; or the Sad Effects of Drunkenness, exemplified in the History of Will and Jean." This chapbook against liquor was written by Hector Macneill and was extremely popular.

Other religious chapbooks are "The Life and Meritorious Transactions of John Knox, the great Scottish Reformer," "The Life and Prophecies of Alexander Peden," "Sins and Sorrows spread Before God: A Sermon," by the Rev. Isaac Watts, "A Choice Drop of Honey, The Rock Christ, or, a short word of advice to Saints and Sinners," by Thomas Wilcocks.

Many, if not all the "Cheap Repository Tracts" were intended especially for use in Sunday schools, and their titles included "The Conversion of St. Paul," "The General Resurrection," "On Carrying Religion into Business," "The Valley of Tears," "Sinful Sally," "The Shopkeeper turned Sailor," "The Election," "A Hymn of Praise," etc. Whether in prose or poetry, the title page that did duty also as the cover page always carried an attractive woodcut illustration. Sometimes there were illustrations in the text. "Sinful Sally" is in verse and Sally in person tells how she was led to become sinful, then drunken and finally to a most melancholy and most hopeless end, thereby serving as a warning to all town and country young women. Upon reading this chapbook, one finds that Sally entered into a life of sin and gaiety, fine clothes, theatres and gin, until disease seized her body and racking pain afflicted her bones.

In "The Gamester," another "Cheap Repository" tract, it is related how Mr. Trickett lost his position by gambling, then nearly caused his wife's death by the same

thing and finally ended in being transported as a convict to Botany Bay. Some of these
tracts were issued serially, one part appearing each month for three or four months.
Such was the case with "Black Giles the Poacher," and "The History of Mr. Bragwell; or
the Two Wealthy Farmers." Black Giles' regular business was rat catching by he lived
mainly by poaching and his family preferred to live by their wits and petty thievery.
Giles, after getting into numerous troubles was finally killed by the falling of a high
wall as he was attempting to steal a net that he thought would be useful in catching
partridges.

Figure 10

A Cheap Repository Tract.

     In all these moral tales, the reader has his attention called repeatedly to the
sinfulness of wrongdoing and to the desirability of living a Christian life.

     Other Cheap Repository Tracts that were popular are "The Shepherd of Salisbury
Plain," "The Happy Waterman," "Daniel in the Den of Lions," "Divine Songs for Children,"
by Dr. Watts, "The Gin Shop" and the "Two Shoemakers." And this short list could be
extended by many additional titles. In "Bibliotheca Somersetensis" by Emanuel Green
there are approximately 200 different titles of these tracts.

Chapter 7

OF HOUSEHOLD CHAPBOOKS

These were not as numerous as other types, but several were very popular. In general they embraced the art of swimming, the brewing of good strong ale and small beer, the best way for a servant maid to gain love and esteem and thereby make both maid and mistress happy, the complete art of cookery, the art of money catching, the shepherd's calendar, the art of amassing riches, and methods of killing adders, badgers, bugs, weasels and worms in gardens.

Although Benjamin Franklin was not a dashing chapbook hero like Monsieur Claude Duval or Jack Sheppard, some of his writings circulated in chapbooks and perhaps were enjoyed by readers serious enough to desire instruction and advice. Franklin's "Way to Wealth" was the principal one to find its way into chapbook literature. The first separate edition of this popular piece was printed and sold by Benjamin Mecom of Boston, in 1760 under the title "Father Abraham's Speech to a Great Number of People, at a Vendue of Merchant-Goods," etc. From 1760 on, "Way to Wealth" pamphlets appeared in numerous cities in America and abroad, and it was translated into thirteen foreign languages. Not all such editions may be classed as chapbooks, but the chapbook printers were not long in adding the title to their series and it was printed in London, Nottingham, Kilmarnock, Newcastle, Derby, Stirling and other places, turning up as late as 1850 in Glasgow.

Apparently chapbook printers were not slow in seeing possibilities in the sale of Franklin's "Way to Wealth" advice. The contents of such chapbook issues were more or less identical, and consisted of abridged printings of many of Poor Richard's maxims and trite sayings with which we are familiar, such as the evils of idleness, the need for industry and saving, the benefits of diligence, etc., the kind of advice once handed out to graduating classes by successful bankers, but which has not been so popular of late years, in view of the fact that savings have disappeared and diligence, seemingly, has a low market value.

Another of Franklin's writings that circulated in chapbook form was his "Advice to Bathers." This was called "The art of swimming rendered easy; with directions to learners. To which is prefixed, Advice to bathers," by Dr. B. Franklin. Judging by the number of extant copies of the "Way to Wealth" in comparison with those containing "Advice to Bathers," the former was by far the most popular, probably because it is more desirable to know how to become wealthy than to know how to swim. Certainly our economic structure is not founded upon a knowledge of swimming.

In "The Pleasing Art of Money Catching and the Way to Thrive by turning a penny to advantage; with a new method of Regulating Daily Expenses," one may find much good advice, such as: "See that your comings in be more than your layings out; for unless this be minded a man may waste away his substance to nothing unsensibly.....Keep an exact account of what you lay out and what you receive; for without this, you will be always in the dark.....In laying out your money, trust not to your servants; for in small matters they may deceive you and you be never the wiser; and many such small matters may amount to a great sum.....Never buy but with ready money; and buy where you find things cheap and good rather than for friendship or acquaintance sake.....Let not thy table exceed the fourth part of your revenue," and so on, not forgetting to "Be sure not to keep company with drunkards and busybodies and all such as are apt to talk much to little purpose."

For the housewife there were such publications as "The Cottage Cook, or, Mrs. Jones's Cheap Dishes; Shewing the Way to do much good with little Money," which

curiously enough happens to be a "Cheap Repository Tract." In this tale, a formerly
wealthy lady tells her minister that she has grown shy of the poor since she has no
money to give them. He tells her that she can give the poor her time and talents, which
would be more effective than money and so she finally does some visiting among the inhabitants of the parish, giving them lessons in domestic economy. At the end of the
account there are four recipes, and some friendly hints like the following: "If you
turn your meet into broth it will go much farther than if you roast or bake it. If the
money spent on fresh butter were spent on meat, poor families would be much better fed
than they are. If the money spent on tea were spent on home-brewed beer, the wife would
be better fed, the husband better pleased, and both would be healthier."

THE

Art of Swimming

RENDERED EASY;

WITH

Directions to Learners.

TO WHICH IS PREFIXED,

Advice to Bathers,

BY

DR B. FRANKLIN

GLASGOW :
PRINTED FOR THE BOOKSELLERS.
81.

Figure 11

A popular chapbook.

        In the black-letter chapbook with the following title, which was published in
London by Will Thackaray, in Duck Lane, near Smithfield in 1673 are found many curious
weather beliefs. "The Shepherd's Prognostication for the Weather, with a brief collection of all the members of man physiognomized, and a judgment upon the signification of
moles on man or woman; also the wheel of fortune, approved and confirmed by science and
the reason of Pythagoras, the most excellent philosopher, by the which you may know all
things that you will demand." Of the weather are many statements like the following:
"If ducks and drakes do shake and flutter their wings when they rise, it is a sign of
ensuing water. If young horses rub their backs against the ground, 'tis a sign of great
drops of rain to follow. If sheep do bleat, play, or skip wantonly, it is a sign of
wet weather. If swine be seen to carry bottles of hay, or straw, to any place and hide
them, it betokeneth rain. When oxen do lick themselves against the hair, it betokeneth
rain to follow shortly after. If cattle, when they do puff, or bellow, do look up to
the sky, it signifieth ensuing rain. If dogs entrails stir, or rumble in his belly, it

is a sign of rain.   If crows or daws, bathe themselves in winter, or if they cry, yealk,
along any shore, more than they are commonly wont to do, then will rain presently follow.   When gouty men, or such as are troubled with any old aches, do feel their joynts
to ake, then rain shortly follows after," etc., etc.

And now for a few fair weather signs.   "If kites be seen to walk and fly together, it is a token of fair weather.   When sheep and goats are seen to joyn, or couple
together late, or in the evening, it prognosticateth fair weather.   If oxen be seen to
lie along upon the left side, it is a token of fair weather.   When the owl scricheth in
foul weather, it is a token of fair weather at hands.   When night-bats shew themselves
in great numbers, or more timely in the evening than they were wont, it is a manifest
token that the next day after will be clear and fair.

Another Will Thackaray production is entitled, "The Husbandman's Practice, or
Prognostication For Ever; as teacheth Albert, Alkind, Haly and Ptolomy, with the shepherd's perpetual prognostication for the weather."   This too is in black-letter and is
one of the many chapbooks issued by Thackaray around 1675.   In this one we find many
curious and old popular ideas, of which a few are set forth.

"Of Christmas Day.--If Christmas Day be on the Sunday, that year shall be a warm
winter, and beginning fast with sorrow; there shall be great winds and tempests.   The
Lent shall be mild, warm, and moist.   The summer, hot, dry, and fair.   The harvest,
moist and cold, much like unto winter.   Wine and corn shall be plenty and good, and
there shall be much honey, and the sheep shall prosper well.   The small seeds and fruits
of gardens shall flourish also.   The old men shall die sore, and especially women that
go with child: peace and quietness shall be plenteous among married folks.

"If Christmas Day fall on a Monday, there shall be a misty winter, neither too
cold nor too warm, the Lent shall be very good, the summer windy, with great stormy
weather in many lands: the harvest good, and much wine, but very little honey, for the
swarms of bees shall die; and many women complain, and sit mourning this year for their
husbands."   And so on for the balance of the week, good and bad times are forecast.

Chapter 8

OF HISTORICAL AND BIOGRAPHICAL CHAPBOOKS

Historical and biographical chapbooks were fairly numerous, and frequently both subjects were combined. As a rule outstanding historical events and national characters were written about in abridged forms. Dougal Graham was probably the author of the most important Scottish historical chapbook, "The History of the Rebellion," which contains many small facts such as would, most likely, be recorded by an eye-witness. Few, if any, of these historical and biographical chapbooks have any literary charm. As a rule they are plain, unvarnished accounts of happenings and personages and without exception, they present the current and generally accepted viewpoints of the period. Unlike most chapbooks, Graham's "History of the Rebellion" was advertised in the columns of the "Glasgow Courant" for September 29, 1746 as follows: "That there is to be sold by James Duncan, Printer in Glasgow, in the Saltmercat, the 2nd Spot below Gibson's Wynd, a Book intituled A full, particular, and true Account of the late Rebellion in the Year 1745 and 1746, beginning with the Pretender's Embarking for Scotland, and then an Account of every Battle, Siege, and Skirmish that has happened in either Scotland or England." Graham's "History" continued to be reprinted in chapbooks until as late as 1850.

Two favorite historical chapbooks were the "History of the Kings & Queens of England from the Reign of William the Conqueror to Victoria the First," and "The History of the Kings & Queens of England and Scotland; from the Reign of James the First to Victoria the First." These were 24-page chapbooks, each page containing a picture of a ruler and a tabloid account of his or her life. J. Catnach issued a much sketchier and more fully illustrated 16-page chapbook on the same subject, entitled "Goldsmith's History of the Kings and Queens of England," in which certain historical events are noted and illustrated, somewhat in the style of the pictures and text of our present "Sunday Supplements." "The Life and Meritorious Transactions of John Knox, the Great Scottish Reformer," and "The History of the Renowned Sir William Wallace" and the "History of the Life and Death, of the Great Warrior Robert Bruce, King of Scotland" circulated among the more studiously inclined readers.

The account of Sir William Wallace starts out as follows: "It was in times of the deepest calamity, when Scotland was overwhelmed with affliction, and sinking into the deepest despair, by the base conduct of an ignominious monarch, that Scotland was betrayed into the hands of the King of England, who put Scotland in a state of cruelty and oppression, and sent blood and carnage over the land that Divine Providence, raised up Sir William Wallace, for a deliverer of his country from the slavish submission to the English monarch, and a champion to avenge her wrongs." Another edition of William Wallace, published by Archibald Paterson, engraver and copperplate printer of Glasgow, is illustrated by grotesque, hand-colored pictures.

Even ancient history appeared in chapbooks, as indicated by "A New Historical Catechism containing Answers to Questions in Ancient History." This contains such things as "Q. What became of Herodias her dancing daughter, who required John the Baptist's head? A. It being reported she had to pass over a frozen river, the ice broke and her head was cut off thereby, without hurting the lady, to the great admiration of all the spectators," "Q. What became of Herod after his persecuting of Christ in his infancy, and slaying the children in Bethlehem? A. He wore out his miserable life and was in continual fear of his own wife and sons, who he afterwards cruelly murdered. He fell into grief and desperation by reason of a loathsome and incurable disease, of which he died; having attempted to stab himself, but was prevented by bystanders."

"The Siege of Troy" printed in London by Sabine and Son, and which sold for sixpence, is an ambitious production of 82 pages that starts with "An account of the parentage, birth and glorious actions of Hercules of Greece; How Hercules strangled two
serpents in his cradle, that had killed his brother; How Hercules conquered two giants
and rescued the king of Troy's daughter, by killing a sea monster," and ends with Brutus
who, after conquering Albion, caused London to be built.

How a rude parcel of ruffians under the leadership of Wat Tyler, a tailor, John
Ball, a minister, and Jack Straw, a thresher, came to London, ransacking and demolish-
ing by the way, and demanded a meeting with the King--is told in that favorite chapbook,
"The History of Wat Tyler and Jack Straw," of which many copies were printed for the
travelling stationers. This gives a fair account of the poll-tax rising of 1381 during
the reign of Richard II, but it characterizes the men who protested against oppression
as rabble, blackguards and scum.

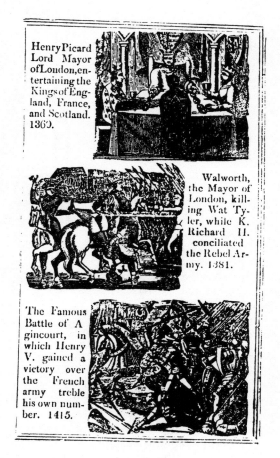

Figure 12

A page from "Goldsmith's History of the Kings and
Queens of England," printed by J. Catnach.

Then there was "The History of the Most Renowned Queen Elizabeth And her great
Favorite the Earl of Essex," taken up mostly with a lengthy confession by Elizabeth to
the Countess of Nottingham, of her love for the Earl of Essex. The chapbook account
which includes many mistakes was taken mainly from "The Secret History of the most renowned Queen Elizabeth and the Earl of Essex. By a Person of Quality, London, 1695."
Sufficiently descriptive of its contents is the chapbook printed by C. Dicey in Bow
Church Yard, entitled "The Conquest of France With the Life and Glorious Actions of

Edward the Black Prince. Son to Edward the Third King of England, his Victory, with about Twelve thousand Archers and Men at Arms, over Philip of France, and an hundred thousand Frenchmen; his Vanquishing King John of France, and taking him and his Son Prisoners; his Love to the Earl of Kent's fair Daughter, and Marriage with her; Being a History full of great and noble Actions in Love and Arms, to the Honour of the English Nation."

Figure 13

King Charles the First.
From a Bow Church Yard chapbook.

Figure 14

Title page of "The History of Mary, Queen of Scots."

As an example of biographical chapbooks we have among others the one published at Newcastle by W. & T. Fordyce on the "History of the Earl of Derwentwater. His Life, Adventures, Trial and Execution.--His Defence when on his Trial in the House of Lords, and his Speech to the People from the Scaffold, previous to his Execution.--Several interesting Particulars of his Death and Burial--his Associates, Lady Derwentwater, and Dilston Castle."

Jack of Newbury, a large cloth maker, who lived during the reigns of Henry VII and Henry VIII, and who entertained Henry VIII and Queen Catherine on their visit to the town, and who contributed liberally to the Church, and of whom little is known, was immortalized in an Aldermary Church-Yard chapbook entitled "The History of Jack of Newbury, Called, The Clothier of England." The chapbook version states that he was apprenticed to a rich clothier of Newbury and wed his master's widow. Their courtship occupies much of the account. Previous to the battle of Flodden, Jack of Newbury supposedly raised 150 men and clothed them at his own expense in white coats, red caps and yellow feathers and led them in the king's army against the Scots. Another such chapbook, also from Aldermary Church-Yard is "The History of Thomas of Reading, And other worthy Clothiers of England. Setting forth Their Mirth, great Riches, and hospitality to the Poor; and the great Favour they gained with their Prince. Concluding with the woeful Death of Thomas of Reading, who was murdered by his Host." Judging from what happened during a dinner that was held for the clothiers at Blossom's Inn, London, some of them must have been regular rowdies.

Other biographies that were peddled by the chapman include the lives of the Duke of Wellington, Mary, Queen of Scots, Princess of Zell, Rory O'More, Marie Antoinette, Lady Jane Gray, Robert Burns, Cervantes, Oliver Cromwell, Paul Jones, etc. Usually, these were drawn from standard accounts, either in whole or in part, retold in simple language, without enthusiasm, and contain little to recommend them. As a rule their extravagant title pages are more interesting than their contents.

It should be stated that chapbooks on the history of battles such as those of Trafalgar, Drumclog, Bothwell Bridge, etc., etc., belong in this group, and also accounts of the corn-laws, rights of man, etc., all of which are now of little interest except to students of historical details. Statesmen or politicians were also topics for chapbooks and as an example of this type, one that was printed in Falkirk in 1823 may be mentioned. This is "Memoirs of the Life of the Right Honourable C. J. Fox, The Man of the People, Secretary of State for the Foreign Department, &c." This is concerned with the life and accomplishments of Mr. Fox from his birth until his death. Fox, of course, was the eminent English statesman, a rival of Pitt, and among other things he opposed his government's policy with respect to American independence.

Chapter 9

OF CHAPBOOKS ON GEOGRAPHICAL DESCRIPTION AND LOCAL HISTORY

To this group belong a small number of chapbooks such as "The History of the castle of the Bastille" published in London, 1790; "Great and new news from Botany Bay," London; "History of Carlisle," Carlisle; "A journey to London in the year 1698; after the ingenious method of that made by Dr. Martin Lyster to Paris in the same year, &c." London, 1699; "The tricks of London laid open," etc., London and others containing descriptions of Ireland, Scotland, etc. They are chiefly informative and are not particularly diverting or amusing. In Falkirk, in 1825, "The History of the Cathedral or

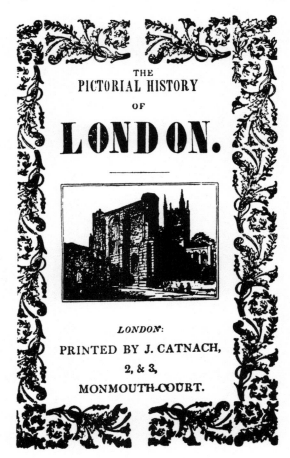

Figure 15

Catnach's "Pictorial History of London."

High Church of Glasgow" was published, covering the time from its foundation in 1136 to 1819. This is a twenty-four-page chapbook that is occupied mainly with the architecture of the cathedral. The last seven pages contain an account of the "Battle of Glasgow." In order to completely fill out the pages, chapbooks frequently contain something that has little or no connection with their main contents. J. Catnach of London printed "The Pictorial History of London" with gayly colored illustrations of Westminster Abbey,

Chelsea Hospital, The Bank of England, The Tower of London, Greenwich Hospital, St. Paul's Cathedral, St. James's Palace, and the Royal Exchange," and the text informs the readers, for example, that 1,100 clerks are employed in the Bank of England and that it is open from nine in the morning until five in the afternoon, holidays excepted. Under the picture of Greenwich Hospital, it is stated that it consists of "a master and governor, a lieutenant-governor, 4 captains and 8 lieutenants, 2,310 pensioners, 149 nurses, and 3,000 out pensioners." We also learn that the site of St. James' Palace was formerly occupied by a hospital founded "for fourteen leprous females, to whom eight brethren were afterwards added." These are only a few of the statements that are recorded.

Pictorial History of London. 3

Th Bank of Eng land.

IN the Year 1732 the first stone of the present building was laid. The Bank of England covers an extent of several acres. It was first incorporated in the Year 1694. There are 1,100 clerks employed in it. The hours of business at the Bank are from nine in the morning till five in the afternoon, holidays excepted. The principal entrance into the Bank is from Threadneedle-street.

Figure 16

Page 3 of "The Pictorial History of London."

At Leeds, J. Johnson printed the "History, Description, and Guide to Kirstall Abbey, (near Leeds) Containing an Account of the Abbey from its Foundation; the Internal Government; List of the Abbots; a Ground Plan of the Building, shewing the various Offices; and the Present State of the Ruins, &c., &c., also, Mary, The Maid of the Inn." Such chapbooks as these probably had only a local circulation and sometimes they were one of a series containing many different kinds of titles.

The "Paisley Repository" sometimes carried something on local history such as "A Guide to Inscriptions sculptured on Tombstones, &c. before the year 1710, in the parishes of Paisley," and also the "Accurate List of those Persons who were unfortunately drowned in the Canal Bason, at Paisley, on Saturday the 10th November 1810, with an additional list of those persons who were on deck when the vessel heeled, and were providentially saved." This latter issue of the "Paisley Repository" is dated February 20, 1811.

Chapter 10

OF CHAPBOOKS ON TRAVEL AND ADVENTURE

One might suppose that travel and adventure would be fertile fields for chapbook authors, but such was not the case. Generally speaking, such subjects were not numerous. However, there were some accounts such as Mandeville's travels, the voyages of Ambrose Guinett, the adventures of sailors, sufferings of deserters, shipwrecks, and escapes from prisons that were enjoyed by chapbook readers.

In the fourteenth and fifteenth centuries, Sir John Mandeville's work was quite popular, and it is not surprising that it found its way, in a very much condensed form, to the chapbook. An Aldermary Church Yard edition is entitled "The Foreign Travels of Sir John Mandeville containing An Account of remote Kingdoms, Countries, Rivers, Castles, &c. Together with a Description of Giants, Pigmies, and various other People of odd Deformities; as also their Laws, Customs, and Manners. Likewise, enchanted Wildernesses, Dragons, Griffens, and many more wonderful Beasts of Prey, &c. &c. &c." Chapter four of the chapbook version is "Of a bloody kind of People; and of People that have heads like Hounds" and it is reprinted as follows: "Not far from the last mentioned place is an island called Tarkonet, inhabited by a wicked kind of people, whose delight is in the slaughter of mankind, whose blood they drink with as much pleasure as if it was the richest wine in the world. Moreover, he is accounted most famous who commits most murders; and if two are at variance they must drink of each other's blood before they can be reconciled.

"Departing from thence, I came to the isle of Macumerac, where the men and women have heads like hounds, and worship the Ox. They fight well, and send the prisoners to their King; who is a peaceable and virtuous man, hindering nobody from passing through his country. About his neck he wears three hundred pearls, with which he says three hundred prayers every morning before breakfast. Here are wild beasts, serpents, &c."

Of course, Sir John Mandeville was a colossal borrower and liar. In fact he never existed, and the personal history in his account is pure invention. Bibliographers tell us that the book was compiled originally by a Liege physician, one Jehan a la Barbe, who obtained his information from works of others. Nothing definite or extensive appears to be known of Barbe and it is not necessary here to go into the current conjectures and suppositions based on incomplete information about him. It has been recorded that only in a small part of the work, treating of the Holy Land, does there appear to be any facts and knowledge obtained by actual travel, and even this appears to be founded upon the travels of William of Boldensele (1336). Much of the portion relating to distant travel was borrowed from a narrative of Friar Odoric, written in 1330, and this Mandeville serves up with additional, extravagant particulars. His Asiatic geography was appropriated from the "Historiae Orientis" of Hetoum; and his information about the Tartars, from the "Speculum historiale" of Vincent de Beauvais. And in addition his account of Prester John came from the famous epistle, widely circulated in the thirteenth century. However, regardless of sources, his borrowings plus his imagination produced a classic that many persons have enjoyed.

Another twenty-four-page travel chapbook that was once sold by E. Tracy at the Three Bibles on London-bridge, and one that was frequently republished, is "The Voyages and Travels of that Renowned Captain, Sir Francis Drake, into the West Indies, and Round about the World: giving a perfect relation of his strange adventures, and many wonderful discoveries, his fight with the Spaniard, and many barbarous nations; his description of monsters, and monstrous people, with many other remarkable passages not before extent, contained in the history of his Life and Death; both pleasant and profitable to the Reader."

        In a twenty-four-page chapbook, printed in Falkirk in 1825, "The Travels   Adventures of Will'm Lithgow in Europe, Asia, and Africa, during Nineteen Years" are set forth, being an abridgment of a larger work. William Lithgow, a Scotsman, walked all over Germany, Bohemia, Switzerland and the Low Countries and lived ten months in Paris, and then set out on foot for Italy in 1609. In the chapbook versions, descriptions are omitted in favor of Mr. Lithgow's adventures, which included beatings and fights with

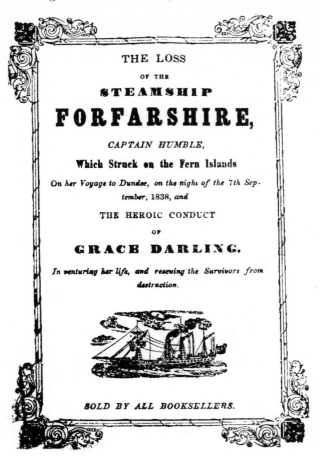

THE LOSS

OF THE

STEAMSHIP

FORFARSHIRE,

CAPTAIN HUMBLE,

Which Struck on the Fern Islands

On her Voyage to Dundee, on the night of the 7th September, 1838, and

THE HEROIC CONDUCT

OF

GRACE DARLING.

In venturing her life, and rescuing the Survivors from destruction.

SOLD BY ALL BOOKSELLERS.

Figure 17

A Steamship disaster title.

robbers, together with happenings that he witnessed. At Venice, as soon as he landed at St. Mark's Place he saw "a great crowd of people, and in the midst of them a great smoke" due to "a grey-friar of the Franciscan order" being burned alive at St. Mark's Pillar, for debauching fifteen noble nuns, and all within a year. Pressing forward, Mr. Lithgow came to the pillar, just as half his body and his right hand fell into the fire. "This friar was forty-six years old, and had been confessor of that nunnery of Sancta Lucia five years. Most of these nuns were Senitors' daughters. Fifteen (all pregnant) were sent home to their father's palaces; the lady prioress and the rest were banished forever; the nunnery was razed to the ground; the revenues were given to the poor, and the church converted to an hospital." so Mr. Lithgow said.

        A much larger chapbook is the 90-page one, printed in Gainsborough in 1812 by H. Mozley--on "The Life and Surprising Adventures of Frederick Baron Trenck" who finally was guillotined in France in 1795. "The Madrid Shaver's Adventures in the Spanish Inquisition," which is always turning up in chapbook collections and with which collectors are so familiar, does not seem to be a true adventure. In all likelihood, it is a piece of entertaining fiction dealing with the somewhat amusing adventures of Nicolas Pedrosa, who followed the trade of shaver, surgeon and midwife in the city of Madrid.

"The Wonderful Adventures of Sixteen British Seamen; also A Cure for the Toothache," printed for the booksellers, Glasgow, is an account of the activities of sixteen sailors who set up as privateers on the Chilian and Peruvian coasts. Because the story would not fill twenty-four pages, the cure for the toothache was appended by the publisher. This and the preceding chapbook appear to have been issued about 1850 or thereabouts.

"The Life and unparalleled Voyages and Adventures of Ambrose Gwinett, formerly well known to the public as the Lame Beggar," printed in London by J. Fairburn, is a melancholy account of Ambrose Gwinett, "who was tried, convicted and hanged at Deal, for the supposed murder of Mr. Collins. His surprising recovery after hanging in chains: His voyages to the West Indies, and being taken by the Spaniards, amongst whom he met with the supposed murdered Mr. Collins. Was taken by the pirates; and retaken by the Spaniards, and after many hardships, returned to England," where he ended his days begging. Appended to this tale is "An Account of the Horrid and Long Concealed Murder of Mr. T. Kidderminster."

Thomas Tegg, of London, to whom reference has been made, published many accounts of marine disasters to sailing vessels which usually sold for six-pence each. These authorless twenty-eight-page accounts were always accompnaied by an engraved folding frontispiece depicting the horrors of shipwrecks. The titles were generally long, one of medium length being "Interesting Particulars of the loss of the American ship Hercules, Capt. William Stout, on the coast of Caffraria, June 16, 1796; the consequent sufferings and subsequent adventures of the crew, during a long and painful journey over the southern regions of Africa, to the Cape of Good Hope, (1809?). As a rule, Plummer of Seething Lane printed these chapbooks for Mr. Tegg.

Another title is "Loss of His Majesty's Ship Centaur, of seventy-four guns, the 23d of September, 1782; and miraculous preservation of the pinnace, with the Captain, Master, and Ten of the Crew. Also the explosion of the French East-India Company's Vessel the Prince, on the 25th of July, 1752, and miraculous preservation of part of the crew in the pinnace. London; Printed for Thomas Tegg, 111 Cheapside." This account states that the Centaur left Jamaica in a leaky condition and ran into a fatal gale. The part of the crew that left the ship were saved while those remaining on board perished. The Prince also was a leaky vessel that caught fire, the flames finally reaching the powder room. Plenty of details make these accounts quite realistic reading and impress one with the dangers of early transportation by water.

Chapter II

OF CHAPBOOKS ON ODD CHARACTERS AND STRANGE EVENTS

Mermaids, misers, miracles, savage girls, dancing furniture, underground dwellers, extraordinary sleepers, deliveries of rabbits, and kings of beggars, all straining at the leash of truthfulness, and some of them getting away entirely, parade through the chapbooks of this group.

Perhaps readers of chapbooks in the eighteenth century believed that two old men were found living underground near the town of Doncaster, in Yorkshire; that Catherine Mewis of Staffordshire was deprived of her eyesight on weekdays and could only see on the Sabbath; that Mary Taft gave birth to rabbits; and that John Robinson talked with a mermaid, all of which are set forth in chapbooks. Even though they didn't believe such accounts, they were certainly supplied with extraordinary reading matter. The following three titles, all of the eighteenth century, speak for themselves.

"A wonderful and Strange Relation of a Sailor in St. Bartholomew's Hospital, London who slept for five days and nights together and then awaking gave an account of the blessedness of those in Heaven, and the woeful estate of the damned in Hell. And also of the state of two of his companions who dy'd whilst he was in his sleep. All of which is attested by the Minister and many who were present and ear witnesses to the relation."

"The Miracle of Miracles. Being a full and true account of Sarah Smith, daughter of John Symons a farmer, who lately was an inhabitant of Darken Parish in Essex, that was brought to bed of a strange monster, the body of it like a fish with scales thereon: it had no legs but a pair of great claws, tallons like a liands, it had six heads on its neck, one was like the face of a man with eyes, nose, and mouth to it, the 2d like the face of a camel, and its ears cropt, two other faces like dragons with spiked tongues hanging out of their mouths, another had an eagles head with a beak instead of a mouth at the end of it, and the last seeming to be a calves head. Which eat and fed for some time, which monster has surprised many thousand people that came there to see it. Daily, spectators flock to view it, but it was by command of the magistrates knock'd on the head, and several surgeons were there to dissect it. Also you have a funeral sermon on the woman who brought it forth, a very wicked liver, and disobedient to her parents, and one that was mightily given to wishing, cursing and swearing. With a prayer before and after the said sermon. It being very fit and necessary to be had in all families for a warning to disobedient children. This strange and unheard of monster was brought into the world in May last, and if any doubt the truth thereof, it will be certified by the minister and church-wardens of said parish of Darkins in Essex as aforesaid."

"The Wonder of Wonders being a strange and wonderful relation of a mermaid, that was seen and spoke with, on the Black Rock nigh Liverpool, by John Robinson Mariner, who was tossed on the ocean for six days and nights; Together with the conversation he had with her, and how he was preserved; with the manner of his death five days after his return home."

John Robinson was the only survivor on the ship Dolphin and the mermaid came aboard and asked "how he did." John said, "I am the better to see you in good health, in great hopes trusting you will be a comfort and assistance to me in this my low condition; and so caught hold of her comb and green girdle that was about her waist. To which she replied, "Sir, you ought not to rob a young woman of her riches, and then expect a favour at her hands; but if you will give me my comb and girdle again, what lies in my power, I will do for you." So he returned the articles and made a date with her for the following Friday. She gave him a compass, told him to steer south-west, and then jumped into the sea. After she had gone, the tempest ceased and the wind blew to the southwest and he finally reached shore and eventually his father's house. As he was worrying about not keeping his date with her, she appeared to him and sang, after which she took the compass, and putting a ring on his finger, disappeared. He was taken ill and died in five days, "to the wonderful admiration of all people who saw the young man."

Illustrated with forty-three woodcuts, there appeared in London, "A Strange and Wonderful Relation of the Old Woman who was drowned at Ratcliff-highway a fortnight ago; to which is added the old woman's dream a little after her death." This was published in two parts and the woodcuts were taken from various sources, including an early edition of Bunyan's "Pilgrim's Progress." A portrait of Queen Elizabeth is included and the title page shows a ducking stool in operation.

"An account of the Surprising Savage Girl, Who was caught running wild in the Woods of Champagne, a Province in France. Containing A true Narrative of many curious and interesting particulars, respecting this very wonderful child of Nature. Translated from the French," was a popular chapbook and various publishers took advantage of its popularity. This savage girl, when first seen, was clothed with rags of skins, her face and hands were black and she was armed with a club. A bull dog was set upon her, but she despatched him neatly with a blow on the head and then jumped over his dead body. She ran up and down trees like a squirrel, ate raw meat and fish, had very large thumbs, and uttered squeaking cries that were frightful. After being captured, and washed, it

Figure 18

Sarah Smith brought to bed
of a strange monster.

Figure 19

M. Bamfyeld Moore Carew
the king of beggars.

was found that after several washings, she was naturally white. She finally became civilized, lost her teeth by eating cooked food, grew another set, lived in various convents, became poor in health, and died. These and many more statements relative to her life are set forth and part of them are supported by an extract from the Baptism Register of the Parish Church of St. Sulplice (sic) of the Town of Chalons, in Champagne.

Another popular chapbook was the "Adventures of Bamfyeld Moore Carew, For more than Forty Years King of the Beggars." Carew was the son of a clergyman who lived in Devonshire. He was born in 1693 and instead of going to the university for which his father was fitting him, he ran away from school and joined a band of gipsies. His begging was highly successful because he disguised himself and imitated so many characters, once a shipwrecked seaman, another time an honest farmer, again, a madman, and on still another occasion, a rat-catcher, also an old woman, a blacksmith down on his luck, a crippled tinsmith, an unfortunate shoemaker, etc., all of which stratagems "gained him high applause and honor in the community of gipsies." He finally resigned his kingship, after reflecting how idly he had spent the prime of his life, and retired "to a neat purchase he had made," and there ended his days beloved and esteemed by all.

Ann Lemoine of White-Rose Court, Coleman Street, London, published in 1801, "The Three Misers," a thirty-six-page chapbook, with an engraved frontispiece, and containing, according to the title page, "The strange and unaccountable Life of Daniel Dancer, Esq. Who died in a sack, though worth upwards of 3000 l. a years. With singular anecdotes of Jemmy Taylor, the Southwark Usurer. To which are added, The Life and Remarkable Death of John Overs; With some Account of his Daughter."

The Three Misers.

THE
STRANGE AND UNACCOUNTABLE
LIFE
OF
DANIEL DANCER, Esq.
WHO DIED IN A SACK,
Though worth upwards of 3000l. a Year.

WITH SINGULAR ANECDOTES
OF
JEMMY TAYLOR,
The Southwark Usurer.

TO WHICH ARE ADDED,
THE LIFE AND REMARKABLE DEATH
OF
JOHN OVERS;
With some Account of his Daughter,
Who was the original Founder of St. Mary Overs' Church in
the Borough ; and the Origin of London Bridge.

London:
Printed by T. Maiden, Sherbourne Lane,
FOR ANN LEMOINE, WHITE-ROSE-COURT, COLEMAN-
STREET, AND SOLD BY T. HURST,
PATERNOSTER-ROW.
1801.

Price Sixpence.

Figure 20

Title page of "The Three Misers."

Mr. Dancer lived with his sister, both of them looking like bundles of old rags, in a miserable hovel. They lived only to save, but Mr. Dancer's dog received a pint of milk daily. In cold weather he stayed in bed to keep warm. He kept a mare, but never allowed her more than two shoes at one time, believing that shoes on her hind feet were unnecessary. He was the most perfect picture of human penury that ever existed and at his death, bank notes and coins were discovered in all corners of his house.

Jemmy Taylor lived raggedly too and slept upon a hard bed, existing upon two-penny fly-blown steaks while he engaged in the business of stock-broking. At his death, his large fortune went to two relatives in the country and his London relatives were forgotten.

John Overs, another fit companion for the two preceding persons, was a ferryman
of London, who acquired great wealth. Too mean to have a fire, he warmed a black pudding in his bosom before eating it, the pudding being heated by his exertions in rowing
over the water. In order to save a day's expenses, he feigned death and while he was
wrapped in a sheet, his servants made merry with food and drink, which so worried him
that he got up and being mistaken for a ghost, received a death blow from an oar in the
hands of one of his scared servants.

Figure 21

Engraved frontispiece to "The Three Misers."
Miss Dancer is greeting her brother upon his good
luck in finding a dead sheep upon the common.

J. Johnson of Leeds, who published many titles in "Johnson's Penny Library," included "The Life of John Metcalf, commonly called Blind Jack of Knaresbro' Containing
many entertaining anecdotes of his exploits in hunting, card playing, &c., also an amusing account of his elopement and marriage to Miss Benson. His Career As A Soldier; Also
a full account of his contracts for making roads, erecting bridges, and other undertak-
ings, which brought him into public notice as a Most Extraordinary Character." This is
a thirty-page chapbook with a picture of a stately blind man on the title page, and the
text retails at considerable length various activities of Mr. Metcalf, in which the blind
do not usually indulge. He was a good swimmer, he rode with the hounds, he acted as a
guide for strangers, he fished and indulged in cock fighting and played the violin, engaged in the stage coach business and even supervised the construction of roads and
small bridges.

Chapter 12

OF PROSE FICTION CHAPBOOKS

Virtue in distress, injured innocence, betrayed virgins, happy brides, lovers' stratagems, heart-broken heroes, swooning heroines, midnight assassins, haunted castles, desolate forests, underground passageways, deserted wings, cold-blooded murders, and more, make their bow in the fiction chapbooks, whose stiff and artificial characters move amid unreal backgrounds. No doubt they furnished many a six-penny thrill to various romantic youths and maidens.

Some of the prose fiction chapbook titles are amusing in themselves. "The love, joy, and distress of the beautiful and virtuous Miss Fanny Adams, that was trapan'd in a false marriage to Lord Whatley," "The history of Amelia; or A description of a young lady who from a great fortune was reduced almost to poverty by an attorney, with an account of her recovering it, for which he was hanged," which happens to be an abridgment of Fielding's novel; "The true and interesting history of Mr. and Mrs. Hartley; or Innocence preserved; showing the fatal effects of jealousy and its baneful influence on the human mind;" and the pathetic sufferings of Louisa Harwood, who was seduced by Lieutenant Harris.....She was necessitated to pawn some of the furniture from her lodgings, for which she was.....tried, convicted, and ordered for transportation &c. &c.....In a letter written to her disconsolate parents."

"The Life of Robinson Crusoe," "The Fortunes and Misfortunes of Moll Flanders," and "The Vicar of Wakefield," all appeared in changed and curtailed chapbook style, sometimes in language that would be too strong for many squeamish stomachs today.

James Hogg's "The Long Pack; a Northumbrian Tale," was popular in chapbooks and appeared under the imprints of many publishers. This is somewhat blood-chilling in spots and is of more interest than many pieces of prose fiction found in chapbooks. It relates to the experience of a servant maid alone in the house during the winter while the family is in London. A pedlar enters, with a peculiar looking pack on his back and endeavors to obtain a night's lodging. This is refused even after he offers the maid a shawl from his pack. After some talk, he gets permission to leave his pack upon two chairs in one of the rooms. It was such a "comical pack" that she couldn't resist looking at it after he had departed and upon one of these visits of inspection she saw it move. Scared, she runs from the house and advises an old servant about the happening, but he is inclined to think that the maid is nervous about nothing. While they are discussing things, a sixteen-year-old cattle herder, employed by the master, arrives on the scene, and anxious to try his gun on something beside crows, he fires at the pack, and "Gracious God! the blood gushed out upon the floor like a torrent, and a hideous roar followed by the groans of death issued from the pack." In the pack with the dead robber were 4 loaded pistols, a cutlass, and a silver "wind-call."

The servants, after the first excitement was over, collected twenty-five men, and sixteen guns, and these were stationed within the house. At midnight the "wind-call" was used and within five minutes a body of horsemen rode up ready to rob the place. However, they were greeted with a burst of gun-fire, that filled four of their number and dispersed the remainder. And so a good plan for robbing the master's home was frustrated.

"The Shepherdess of the Alps," was another chapbook favorite. A young and beautiful widow, whose husband was killed in war, resolves to remain in solitude with her sheep, until united in death with her husband. She is courted by another man, who finally wins her after many touching scenes. Needless to say, the heroine had an "elegant shape and air," although "affliction had added paleness, and faded, in some degree, the blooming carnation of her cheeks."

On a hot and sultry summer day, a young knight, as was customary with young knights, was riding along the forest path of an old wood, deep in meditation. Suddenly he was aroused by a shriek and loud cries for help. He clapped spurs to his steed and galloped in the direction from whence the cries proceeded. In an open glade he beheld a woman, pardon me, a lady, with whom none could vie in grace of form and beauty of face, struggling violently with two men, who were attempting to drag her away. It was but the work of an instant for the knight to cleave one of the ruffians to the ground. The other escaped. This was the beginning of a beautiful friendship and love which, however, ended in the death of both through no fault of their own. For the sorrowful details of this story one should consult "The Fatal Stroke or the Unfortunate Lovers," a penny history in twenty-four pages.

Figure 23

The fair Moll Flanders.

Figure 22

A chapbook Robinson Crusoe.

"Dorastus and Fawnia," the second title of Robert Greene's "Pandosto; or, The Triumph of time," was printed in Aldermary Church Yard and other places under the chapbook title of "The History of Dorastus and Faunia. Setting forth their Loves, Misfortunes, And happy Enjoyment of each other at last," frequently illustrated by grotesque woodcuts. And so on the list could be extended to include the adventures of a young lady who was confined in the hollow of an oak tree, the history of Goody Two-Shoes, the remarkable and entertaining history of a reclaimed lady of pleasure, the story of the bewitched fiddlers, the unfortunate pastry cook, and romances translated from the German, or from the works of M. Voltaire.

Along about 1800 when the chapmen were numerically of but small account but with the chapbook tradition still continuing, there appeared chapbooks of a somewhat better kind, selling for sixpence, and a shilling. These ranged in thickness from twenty-four to seventy-two or more pages. They usually had green or blue, thin paper covers, and in addition there was an engraved frontispiece, sometimes colored, sometimes folding. These productions for the mostpart imitated, or tried to imitate, the style of Mrs. Radcliffe, "Monk" Lewis, and Horace Walpole, and many were the tales turned out by nameless literary hacks for the edification of their readers. Some were frank abridgments and steals from previously published books, with new names for the characters. Many

were abridged and translated from the German. These Gothic tales always carried an ir-
resistible title page, which often served as a synopsis of the story, and T. and R.
Hughes, Dean & Munday, Orlando Hodgson, and Hodgson and Co. were among the chief publishers in London, the most important centre of production.

In "The Treacherous Danish Knight; or, The Border Lords, and the White Plume.
A Beautiful and Original Romance. Including the affecting Tale of Edith, The Forester,"
the engraved and colored frontispiece shows Edith in the forest, with a bundle of fag-
gots, being approached by Sir Guthred. This gentleman was proud, haughty and cruel, one
who would slay his enemy and then drink his blood. No good came of the infatuation of
Sir Guthred for the fair Edith and after a page or two he seized her, imprinted a burning kiss on her feverish lips and hurried her away to the castle. All went well for
about a half page, then he turned her out and she was left to whatever fate might come.
After many pages and more villanies, Sir Guthred fell upon his sword and expired, a
fitting end for an unprincipled wretch.

THE

Imprisoned Chief;

OR, THE

DELUDED MONARCH:

An Historical Romance.

IN WHICH IS POURTRAYED THE

Character of a Treacherous Friend

IN THE PERSON OF

EARL LOMOND,

Who, stung with envy at the superior Endowments of Sigismund

EARL OF MORTON,

Fabricates a vile Tale to the prejudice of that Nobleman; who, in
consequence of Bribery and Perjury, is convicted and

IMPRISONED FOR HIGH TREASON,

BUT, THROUGH THE ENTERPRISING FORTITUDE OF

THE FAIR MARIAN,

The Imprisoned Chief is restored to Liberty
and Love,

The King is undeceived, and the perfidious Calumniator's
Treachery recoils upon himself.

LONDON:

PRINTED AND PUBLISHED BY J. BAILEY, 116, CHANCERY LANE.

Price Sixpence.

Figure 24

A Gothic romance.

Figure 25

Engraved frontispiece to
"The Imprisoned Chief."
"The beautiful Marian discovering
herself to her lover."

"The Imprisoned Chief; or, the Deluded Monarch: An Historical Romance. In
which is pourtrayed the Character of a Treacherous Friend in the person of Earl Lomond,
Who stung with envey at the superior Endowments of Sigismund, Earl of Morton, Fabricates
a vile Tale to the prejudice of that Nobleman, who in consequence of Bribery and Perjury, is convicted and imprisoned for high treason, but through the enterprising fortitude of The Fair Marian, The Imprisoned Chief is restored to Liberty and Love, The King

is Undeceived, and the perfidious Calumniator's Treachery recoils upon himself." Here
we have a complete synopsis and the details may be spared.

Other titles not so full and explanatory, but designed to excite the interest
are, "Fatal Jealousy; or, Blood Will Have Blood! containing the history of Count Almagro
and Duke Alphonso; Their combat in the dreadful tournament, and the death of the beautiful Bellarmine, through the artifice of Sophronia, her rival;" "Parental Murder; or The
Brothers, An interesting romance; in which Virtue and Villany are Contrasted and followed by Reward and Retribution;" "The Old English Baron; A Gothic Story. From an ancient manuscript. By Clara Reeve." This title page is prefaced by a statement from
the publisher to the effect that "The following story, a confessed imitation of the

THE

PERUVIAN DÆMON;

OR,

CONJUGAL CRIMES.

CONTAINING

SCENES OF TERROR

IN THE

MOORISH CASTLE OF HONARDO,

AND THE

BANDITTI CHAMBER

OF THE

ALPINE MOUNTAINS.

'Twas his the mask of Pleasure to assume,
And thus allure her vot'ry to his doom;
Till the poor wretch, envelop'd in his chain,
Sees sensual pleasure prove eternal pain.

LONDON:

PRINTED FOR T. AND R. HUGHES. 35, LUDGATE-HILL,
CORNER OF STATIONERS-COURT.
Lewis and Hamblin, Paternoster-row.

1807.

Figure 26

"The Peruvian Daemon."

Castle of Otranto was first printed at Newcastle in an evening paper," etc., etc., a
most unusual thing for a chapbook; "Florian De Videmont, Chieftain of the Blue Castle;
or Lorenzo, the starving prisoner, and The Saviour of Almagro and His Two Daughters from
the horrors of The Red Chamber;" and "The Peruvian Daemon; or Conjugal Crimes. Containing Scenes of Terror in the Moorish Castle of Honardo, and the Banditti Chamber of the
Alpine Mountains;" "Cordelia, or The Heiress of Raymond Castle. A Romance. By Frances
Mary Ryder."

In "The Mystery of the Black Convent. An interesting Spanish Tale of the
Eleventh Century," we are told that "in a remote part of Old Castile, surrounded by

lofty mountains, and begirt with shadowy groves, stood the once stupendous monastery of St. Lawrence, a pile of gloomy architecture, inhabited by Monks of the order of Carthusians." To this monastery in 1140 came a young man of elegant and engaging manners with the idea of excluding himself from the world and "of preparing for the perfections of a future state." This young man St. Alme was accepted and for three years he was serene and composed. Then discontent clouded his brow and he was always absorbed in melancholy abstraction. The Superior diagnosed St. Alme's trouble as love and cautioned him against the indulgence of his passions. Upon talking to one of the friars about St. Alme's changed disposition, this friar suggested that he observe St. Alme's conduct during his moments of privacy. And during this peeping he saw St. Alme gaze upon a picture until tears came to his eyes, and, "As the mourner lay extended on the pallet, the inquisitive Monk observed, with increased astonishment, the throbbing bosom of a Woman,

Page 26

YALDUF *bearing in his Arms* LAURETTE.

Pubᵈ as the Act directs by T&R Hughes 35 Ludgate Stᵗ

Figure 27

Engraved frontispiece to "The Peruvian Daemon."

revealed through the aperture which her unguarded desperation had occasioned!" and "As he gazed on the recumbent female, he saw a thousand beauties which had hitherto escaped his observations; he felt that the resolution of the puritan was fast receding." With the knowledge he had gained this friar sought the cell of the fair incognita and declared himself the slave of her attractions, but alas, he was repulsed. Additional spying on the part of the friar brought to light the fact that the lady was meeting someone in the church yard vault. He followed her and was about to accost her when a third person made his appearance and caused the lady to shriek aloud and swoon in terror. The friar fled and told every friar in the monastery of his suspicions, with the result that

they all trooped to the vault and dragged forth "the astonished female and her suspected paramour." All of this was brought to the attention of the Superior and it eventually turned out that the paramour was the lady's father who had entered the monastery.
The lady had wanted to see him and knew of no other way than to disguise herself as a
man. She had also been unhappy with her husband and was quite content to get away from
worldly troubles. Her father, instead of being dead, had only been in a trance, and she
had gone to the vault for a final glimpse of him. And so everything ended happily and
the peeping friar, seeing that "his disgrace was likely to be the issue of his malevo-
lence, in gloomy disappointment, he left the presence of the Superior."

        And so they flourished, for a period, these chapbooks, with their tales of ter-
ror, of hearts cleft in twain, of convents, of Gothic castles, of melancholy heroes, of
swooning maidens, of low browed villains, of bluebeard barons, of cruel monks, of stony
hearted parents, and with their complicated plots, exaggerated characters, and flowery
diction. And it must be said too, with their engraved frontispieces depicting some sen-
sational aspects of the tales, with grotesque stiffness. These Gothic chapbooks flourished until about 1825, when they were superseded by monthly magazines with stories that
were more consistent and better written.

Chapter 13

OF PROSE CHAPBOOKS ON LEGENDARY ROMANCES, FAIRY TALES, AND FOLK TALES

In these chapbooks, of which there were a great many, a galaxy of familiar personages appears. Aladdin, Ali Baba, Cinderella, Blue Beard, The Children in the Wood, Hector, Prince of Troy, Jane Shore, Fair Rosamond, Fortunatus, Guy, Earl of Warwick, Little Red Riding Hood, Robin Hood, the Sleeping Beauty, Jack the Giant Killer, Reynard the Fox, Jack and the Beanstalk, Sir Bevis, the Seven Wise Masters, Thomas Hickathrift, Valentine and Orson, Whittington and his Cat, and many others of equal or lesser fame enter the stage and perform for the amusement of their readers. Many of these are such familiar characters that it would appear to be unnecessary to give more than a few examples. To me this group is the most interesting of all the groups making up chapbook literature, and it would be of interest to trace some of the tales to their obscure sources and to show the changes that have taken place in their illustrations and in their versions over a period of time, but this would require a separate book.

As an example of the backgrounds of many fairy tales it may be of interest to deal with "Jack the Giant Killer" at some length. Although it may seem incredible, there are actually some people so old that they either have forgotten the adventures of Jack the Giant Killer, or have him hopelessly confused with Jack and the Bean Stalk, and so for the purpose of setting these unfortunates straight, it may be well to review, briefly, the "pleasant and delightful history of Jack and the giants."

Jack, the son of a wealthy farmer, flourished during King Arthur's time, in England, which country suffered from the thieving propensities of a race of dumb but troublesome giants. His first adventure consisted in outwitting the giant Cormoran, of Mount Cornwall, by digging a pit, into which Cormoran fell, and then neatly dispatching him by a blow on the head from a pick-axe. The news of this outrage reached the giant Blunderboar, who lived in an enchanted castle in Wales, and Jack was unfortunate enough to fall into Blunderboar's hands. He was locked in a room of the castle while Blunderboar hunted up his brother so that both could enjoy the killing. However, Jack found two strong cords in his room, and while the giants were unlocking the gate, he managed to get running nooses over their heads and of course they died of strangulation. Next, a Welsh giant, with two heads, who appeared friendly, invited Jack to a room in his house, and Jack would surely have lost his life in the night had he not substituted a billet of wood for himself, in bed, which billet the giant struck with a greaty knotty club. The next morning at breakfast, Jack, instead of eating four gallons of hasty pudding, managed to slip it into a leather bag under his coat, then telling the giant he [wou]ld show him a trick, he ripped the bag open and the pudding plopped out. The giant, [wishing t]o imitate such a delightful trick, ripped open his own scrobiculus cordis, his [guts a]nd trullibubs" fell out and that was the end of him.

[J]ack then met King Arthur's son and both of them visited a three-headed giant [with] a tremendous reputation as a fighter. Jack, however, so scared this giant by [telling] him that the King's son with a thousand men was on his way to kill him, that [the giant] begged Jack to lock him up in a vault until the prince had departed. This [was done] and the grateful giant presented him with a coat which would make the wearer [invisibl]e, a pair of shoes of incredible swiftness, a cap of knowledge and a sword [to cut] asunder whatever it struck. With this magic equipment, Jack outwits evil [giants] who had enchanted a beautiful lady, thereby making it possible for the prince [to wed h]er. All then return to the court of King Arthur, where Jack is received with [honor] and made one of the Knights of the Round Table.

Jack then adopted giant-killing as a vocation, and after being supplied with money and a horse, he started out to rid the realm of "cruel and devouring monsters." Against his magic trappings the giants did not have the ghost of a chance. He cut off giants' legs, noses and heads, rescued worthy knights and fair ladies, distributed treasures, outwitted the two-headed Thunderful, author of "Fe, Fi, Fo, Fum " etc., and sent his heads to King Arthur. But his crowning achievement was the slaughter of Galligantus who collaborated with a conjurer in transforming knights and ladies, including a duke's daughter, into "sundry shapes." Jack passed the fiery griffins, wearing his invisible coat, and having reached the gate of the castle he blew a golden trumpet which hung there. This caused the castle to tremble, and just as Galligantus stooped to pick up his club, Jack decapitated him with his sword of sharpness. The conjurer was carried off by a whirlwind, the castle vanished and the knights and ladies assumed their proper forms. Upon their return to the Court of King Arthur, Jack married the duke's daughter and lived happily ever after in "a noble house, with a large estate."

This brief and inadequate summary does not, of course, give one any idea of Jack's cunning over the stupid giants, of his ready wit, of his entertaining conversations with the giants, of how he liberated fair ladies, of how the giants ate men's hearts and livers with pepper and vinegar, of the dreadful shrieks which emanated from knights and ladies being held by the hair of their heads, of the terrible appearance of some of the giants, with eyes of fire and cheeks like sides of bacon; for these, one must consult a version which has not been softened by the Society for the Supervision of Children's Reading, or whoever it is that does such things.

The oldest edition of this nursery tale appears to be one dated 1711, supposedly in the British Museum, entitled "The History of Jack and the Giants" (12 mo. n.d.). "The Second Part of Jack and the Giants, giving a full account of his victorious Conquests over the North Country Giants, destroying the Enchanted Castle kept by Galligantus, dispers'd the Fiery Griffins, put the Conjuror to flight, and released not only many Knights and Ladies, but likewise a Duke's Daughter, to whom he was honourably married." (12 mo. Newcastle, 1711) This edition is illustrated by rude woodcuts, representing the important events of the history. The tale was current, however, long before 1711. In "King Lear" (c. 1605) Edgar as Mad Tom says:

Figure 28

Title page illustration from "Jack and the Giants,"
printed by J. White, Newcastle, 1711.

> "Child Rowland to the dark tower came;
> His words were still "Fee, fow and fum!
> I smell the blood of a British man."

And in "Have with you to Saffron Walden," 1596, by Nash, there is mentioned "a precious apothegmaticall pedant who will finde matter inough to dilate a whole daye of the first invention of

> "Fy, fa, fum,
> I smell the bloud of an Englishman!"

Sir Francis Palgrave believed that Jack the Giant Killer was one of the popular stories founded upon King Arthur and his adventures, although certain features of the latter are to be found in popular Asiatic tales. In Malory's "Morte d'Arthur" (1485), Arthur's fight with the giant of St. Michael's Mount is told in frightful detail. Malory's sources were French and English, and to them he added detail and his own interpretation.

Although Arthur figures as a successful general in the "Historia Britonum" (c.810) by Nennius, who expanded and redacted preexisting compilations, Geoffrey of Monmouth is usually called the father of Arthurian romance. Geoffrey, for his "Historia Regum Britanniae," published about 1136, gathered his material, according to L. C. Paton, from "episodes in the chronicles of his contemporaries, William of Malmesbury, and Henry of Huntingdon, from ancient Celtic records, the legends of Celtic saints, Celtic myth, Biblical history, classical and Sandinavian stories, the universal stock of folk-tales, local British tradition, the Carolingian cycle, familiar facts of general history, and from events in the life about him."

In chapter III, Book X, of the "Historia," King Arthur meets on Mount Michael the giant who had captured Helena, niece of Duke Hoel.

The King forthwith unsheathed his sword, and covering him with his shield, hurried as swiftly as hurry he might to be beforehand with him, and prevent his getting hold of the club. But the giant, not unaware of his intentions, had clutched it and smote the King upon the cover of his shield with such a buffet as that the sound of the stroke filled the whole shore, and did utterly deafen his ears. But Arthur, thereupon blazing out into bitter wrath, lifted his sword and dealt him a wound upon his forehead, from whence the blood gushed forth over his face and eyes in such sort as well-nigh blinded his sight. Howbeit, the blow was not deadly, for he had warded his forehead with his club in such wise as to scape being killed outright. Natheless blinded as he was with the blood welling forth, again he cometh on more fiercly than ever, and as a wild boar rusheth from his lay upon a huntsman, so thrust he in within the sweep of Arthur's sword, gripped him by the loins, and forced him to his knees upon the ground. Howbeit, Arthur, nothing daunted, soon slipped from out his clutches, and swiftly bestirring him with his sword, hacked the accursed monster, first in one place and then in another, and gave him no respite until at last he smote him a deadly buffet on the head, and buried the whole breadth of his sword in his brain-pan. The abhorred beast roared aloud and dropped with a might crash like an oak torn up by the roots in the fury of the winds. Thereupon the King brake out on laughing, bidding Bedevere strike off his head and give it to one of the squires to carry to camp as a rare show for sightseers.

The English version of Jack the Giant Killer is also said to have been adapted from the story of Corineus the Trojan, found in Geoffrey's "History of the Kings of Britain."

It has been stated that the earliest form of Jack the Giant Killer in western lore is probably the account of Thor and the giant Skrymir, found in the collection of the celebrated Icelandic historian, Snorri Sturluson, known as "Edda Snorra" (between

1140 and 1160). In this old Scandinavian folk-tale entitled "Thor's Journey to the Land of Giants," Thor becomes enraged because he cannot open the giant's bag, which contains their provisions, and hurls his hammer at the head of the sleeping giant. This awakens Skrymir, who asks if a leaf has not fallen upon him. A second time Thor uses his hammer driving it into the giant's brain, upon which the giant again awakens and asks if an acorn has not fallen on his head. A third time, Thor buries his hammer in the giant's cheek, with the result that Skrymir again is aroused from his sleep and asks if some moss has not fallen on him. Later in the tale it appears that in every case the sly Skrymir had substituted a rock for his person and so escaped the blows from Thor's hammer. This story is similar to that of Jack's adventure with the Welsh giant, and Ashton cites this similarity as part of the proof of the northern origin of Jack the Giant Killer. As for Jack's coat which rendered him invisible, his cap of knowledge, his shoes of swiftness and his miraculously sharp sword, Ashton states:

> To show the northern origin of this tale, it is only necessary to point out that the coat is identical with the magic garment known in ancient German as the "Nebel Kappe," or cloud cloak, fabled to belong to King Alberich and the other dwarfs of the Teutonic Cycle of Romance, who clad therein, could walk invisible. To them also belongs the "Tarn Hut," or Hat of Darkness. Velent, the smith of the Edda of Saemund, forged a "Sword of Sharpness," which in the Wilkina Saga is called Balmung. It was so sharp that when Velent cleft his rival, AEmilius, it merely seemed to the latter like cold water running down him. "Shake thyself," said Velent. He did so, and fell in two halves, one on each side of the chair. The Shoes of Swiftness were worn by Loke when he escaped from Valhalla.

Thomas Keightley, who wrote long before Ashton, called attention to the fact that Jack's strategy, in substituting a stick of wood for himself during his adventure with the Welsh giant, was not peculiar to English giant-killers, but was found also in the folk-tales of other countries. In addition to the tactics of Skrymir, Keightley mentions the German "Brave Tailorling" ("Das tapfere Schneiderlein") which deals with the adventures of a little tailor who had killed seven flies on his bread, all at one blow, and who was so proud of this that he wanted the whole world to know about it, although he was careful to state only that he had killed seven, not specifying what the seven had been. At the beginning of his travels he met a giant sitting on the top of a mountain, and after a comparison of feats in which both giant and tailor performed and in which the tailor came off best, by reason of his tricks, the giant invited him to spend the night in his cave. The tailor was smart enough not to lie in the bed but to hide in a corner instead, and it was well that he did so, for the giant came in during the night and with an iron club struck the bed a blow that sent the club through it. Keightley, after calling attention to the similar strategy of the giant Skrymir and the little tailor, suggests the possibility of Jack the Giant Killer having been brought into England by Anglo-Saxon or Danish ancestors by way of "Thor's Journey to the Land of Giants," and Sir Walter Scott believed that "Jack" landed in England from the very same keels and warships which conveyed Hengist and Horsa, and Ebba the Saxon,"[1] supposedly about 450-455. However, the device of substitution" is found in the folk-tales of more distant countries, and this is noted by Keightley.

In the Persian story, "Ameen of Isfahan and the Ghool," supposedly from India, Ameen saves his life by the substitution of a pillow for himself, in bed, escaping a terrible blow from the Ghool's walking-stick which was as big as the trunk of a tree.

In Perrault's tale of "L'Adroite Princesse," Finetta manufactures a straw figure into which she puts a bladder of blood. Substituting this figure for herself, in bed, she escapes the sword of the prince. And in Giambatista Basile's "Il Pentamerone" (c. 1637, Naples), "Sapia the Glutton," heroine of the tale so called, makes a figure of pastry and sugar scented with musk. This she places between the bed sheets and then hides herself behind a screen. The prince Torre, whom Sapia had given much cause for worry, enters with murder in his heart and plunges a dagger into the confection. So

---

[1] "The Child and His Book," by Mrs. E. M. Field (London, 1892).

terrible was he, that, desiring even to drink her blood, he licks the dagger, but tasting its sweetness and the scent of musk, he is overcome for having killed so sweet a girl and would have taken his own life on the spot had not Sapia come forth to console him.

According to Keightley, most of the circumstances of "Ameen of Isfahan and the Ghool," of "The Brave Tailorling" and of "The Goat and the Lion," one of the stories in "The Panchatantra," which assumed shape in India and spread through Persia, Arabia, Syria and European countries and whose already old tales were supposedly composed about 200 B.C. in Kashmir, are found in "The Lion and the Ass," one of the tales in Straparola's "Pleasant Nights." From this one may assume that the fable of "The Lion and the Ass" originated in India.

In "Notes and Queries" (3rd Ser. IX, pp. 515-16, 1866), H. C. advanced the opinion that the earliest form of Jack the Giant Killer in Western folklore was probably the tale of Thor and the giant Skrymir, and stated that in the East every Hindu school-boy knew of Beeman, one of the five Pandus, and his giant-killing adventures, the Pandus being first mentioned in the "Mahabharata," written at least 240 B.C. He also stated that the words "Fe, fi, fo, fum, I smell the blood of a man," were paralleled in a couplet spoken by a giantess in a Mohammedan tale called "Sunebal [golden-haired] and the Ogress," which he heard related in India.

Although there is a stronger human element in Jack the Giant Killer than in the strictly eastern tales of fairies, genii, etc., giant legends are common in Asia and Europe. The cannibalistic, skin-clothed, stupid giants, armed with clubs and stones, may have been the savage tribes transformed into giants in the folk-lore of those who conquered them.

From the summary herewith presented, one may make the somewhat indefinite statement that Jack the Giant Killer is apparently of Indo-European origin and was probably introduced into England during the Saxon invasion.

Numerous English editions of Jack the Giant Killer have appeared since the one referred to as having been published at Newcastle in 1711. Many are illustrated with delightfully crude woodcuts, sometimes frightfully and carelessly colored in red, blue, green and yellow. Bound in colored paper covers with their pictures of giants in various poses and succumbing to Jack's ingenuity, they must have delighted their juvenile readers immensely. Although the various early editions differ from each other, sometimes in their wording, their omissions and their abridgments, the versions are, for the most part, the same, and the essentials of the tale are retained. In some of the early editions, especially those intended for small children, Jack's sprightly conversation and exchange of wit with a local clergyman, in the opening part of the tale, are omitted. Nowadays one may purchase beautifully printed, bound copies of Jack the Giant Killer, illustrated by such artists as Margaret Campbell Hoopes, Hugh Thomson, H. M. Brock, Margaret W. Tarrant, Margaret Evans Price and others, and it is interesting to note the conceptions of the various illustrators over the two-hundred-year period. For the most part, the giants have maintained their brutish, unintelligent appearance, and Jack remains a dapper hero. These modern versions are essentially like the older ones. Here and there, expressions have been changed or omitted, and killings have been softened somewhat; sometimes the tales are abridged, and on the whole they are a little less concerned with all of the details found in the chapbook versions. During the passage of time the few coarse expressions of the early accounts have disappeared.

If perchance you wish to see the wicked triumph, as they often do, or a foolish bargain lead to ruin, as it usually does, don't read "Jack and the Bean-Stalk," because this is a tale wherein the wicked get their just deserts and where a foolish bargain leads to riches. If it ended otherwise, it, most likely, would not now be a minor masterpiece, nor would it have appealed for so many years to the persons who select children's reading matter. This folk-tale, abounding as it does in magic beans, a fairy, a giant, an enchanged harp, is an example of primitive literature, and one may accept it, as a child, at its face value, or one may look further and detect therein traces of primitive ideas and beliefs.

Recalling the chief happenings of the tale, Jack is the spoiled, only child of a poor widow who is compelled to sell her cow in order to buy food. Jack, on his way to the next village with the cow, meets a butcher who induces him to exchange the animal for some colored beans. Upon his return home, Jack's beans are kicked out of the house in a passion by the angry mother and they both retire supperless to bed. The next morning Jack found that the beans had sprouted and grown so high he could not see the tops of the stalks. He climbs the stalks for hours, finally reaching the top, where he finds himself in a strange country. Here he meets a fairy who tells him that the land is inhabited by a giant who had killed his father and who had stolen his inheritance. Jack comes to the castle and is hidden by the giant's wife. He steals the giant's hen, which lays golden eggs, and returns home. On another visit Jack steals the giant's gold and silver and on a third visit his magic harp. Upon being pursued down the bean-stalk by the giant, Jack reaches the ground first and cuts the stalk so that the giant comes crashing to the earth and is killed.

The "foolish bargain" which Jack made is the basis of many folk-tales. Sometimes it leads to riches and sometimes to ruin. Likewise the talking harp, the death of the giant and the animal which produces gold are all to be found in other well-known fairy tales. The bean-stalk, however, which reaches from the earth to an unknown land, presumably heaven, appears to be a portion which was borrowed from an earlier tale to supply additional interest.

According to Macculloch there are Tuscan, Breton, Lorraine and Flemish variants of a tale wherein a poor man plants a bean which grows until it reaches heaven. He climbs it, and meets St. Peter who presents him with magical objects. In certain Slavonic tales, there is a land beyond the sky peopled by rich and powerful super-beings. This land is visited by a few favored mortals who return with gifts. In some cases it is a cabbage which grows to the sky, in others, a bean or a pea. Such Slavonic tales indicate the existence of a primitive myth about the world above the sky and its inhabitants and the means of reaching that upper region. And certain savage folk-tales suggest the form that the myth may have taken.

In a Dyak tale there is a great tree which grows out of the sky, its branches just touching the water of a whirlpool. In an Australian legend heaven is reached from the summit of a lofty mountain, spirit messengers conveying the visitors hither. The Maoris have a story in which a spider's web serves as a communicating avenue and the Algonquins a tale in which a basket descends from the sky. Many other myths could be cited, ancient Greek, early Egyptian, Chinese, Japanese, etc., in which are incorporated the supposed relations between the earth and the world above the sky and the means of communication. In the Bible, the stories of Jacob's Ladder and the Tower of Babel are examples of primitive beliefs as to how to reach heaven. Thus Jack and the Beanstalk may be traced to man's fanciful way of explaining the region beyond the sky and a method of reaching it and is an instance of how a fantasy may finally become a folk-tale.

As usual, adapters and arrangers have tinkered with the details of the tale, all, of course, with the idea of improving it or of making it a vehicle for the conveyance of their own pet beliefs. The earliest edition of Jack and the Beanstalk which I could find is entitled "The History of Jack and the Bean Stalk." It was printed by G. Caldwell, Bookseller at Paisley, and the British Museum Catalogue suggests 1810 as the date of publication. There must be other editions much earlier than this one. It is a prose version and the story is simply told. The only illustration is a woodcut on the first cover page.

In 1818 Dean and Munday (London) brought out "The Surprising History of Jack and the Bean-Stalk," 34 pages, 5½" by 3½", yellow paper covers, with a folding colored frontispiece 13½" by 5½", containing eight, hand-colored copper engravings. Apparently another edition was published probably two years later by this firm under the title

"Jack and the Bean-Stalk; a Fairy Tale, with elegant coloured engravings....." About this same time, 1820, A. Paterson, 5 King Street, Glasgow, published "The History of Jack and the Bean Stalk" 16 pages, 4⅛" by 2⅝" with nine woodcut illustrations including one on each outside wrapper. This sold for one penny and the prose version, with some omissions, is similar to that of the Paisley (1810?) edition.

In 1854 there appeared George Cruikshank's Fairy Library containing "Hop o' My Thumb," "Jack and the Bean-Stalk" and "Cinderella," all delightfully illustrated by Cruikshank at his happiest. Cruikshank tampered considerably with the original text, adding much new material, and changing details as he went along. He gives Jack a sister, makes the butcher pay Jack for the cow and then cheat him out of the money in a game of chance, brings Jack's father back to life and to the bosom of his family, puts the Giant to work in the royal quarry, and injects his own opinions into the tale, such as, "It is not poverty which makes people dirty, but idleness and ignorance."

When this and the other tales were first published, Cruikshank was subjected to criticism because he had altered them "in conformity with certain philanthropic principles, and especially in the cause of temperance." Charles Dickens especially resented such changes and and embodied his criticism in an article, "Frauds on the Fairies," which was published in "Household Words."

Hallam Tennyson's version in English hexameters adheres to the original and is illustrated with Randolph Caldecott's delicate unfinished sketches. This was published in 1886.

In the dozen or so versions which are in circulation today, the incidents of the tale are for the most part the same as those which were published a hundred or more years ago. In one, the giant's wife is disposed of by having her fall downstairs to her death, and in another the giant is killed by a whirlwind of stones which a fairy causes to fly about his head. However, the deviations are not pronounced and for this tale at least the passion for improving seems to have passed. Nearly all present-day editions of "Jack and the Bean-Stalk" are wonderfully illustrated with colored pictures such as the child of the early nineteenth century never even dreamed about.

"The History of the most noble marquis of Salus; or, Patient Grissel," an Aldermary Church Yard chapbook of twenty-four pages, contains a widespread story that has come to us from the Middle Ages, and it was brought within reach of the masses by numerous writers of penny histories. It is found in Boccaccio's "Decameron." Chaucer made it one of his Canterbury Tales and first introduced it to English readers, and there are also other early references to it. In an abbreviated form it appeared in chapbooks as early as 1703 and in ballad style, even before 1557. The story is concerned with the extraordinary patience of a wife and the brutal behavior of a husband and nowadays the patience of Griselda is a commonplace of literature. The prose of the chapbook, however, is quite different from that of Chaucer.

In the case of "The Pleasant History of Thomas Hickathrift," there was a traditional version long before the story appeared in print in chapbook form or from the sixteenth century on. Tom was the obstinate son of poor parents. After the loss of his father he at first sits in the chimney-corner and does not help his mother. Being of great size and height, he commits many pranks such as throwing a hammer a great distance. He also kills a giant with a club using a wheel for a shield, finally taking possession of the giant's land and living there. He commits more pranks, escapes from four thieves and is defeated by a tinker. In this tale there are incidents that parallel similar incidents in the Scandinavian story of "Grettir the Strong" making it seem that the English form really has a Scandinavian skeleton for its support. However, Thomas Hickathrift was popular with chapbook publishers, running stationers and readers.

A Lord Mayor of London early in the fifteenth century, Sir Richard Whittington, managed to achieve a certain popularity long after his death, by getting into chapbooks that remained in circulation for many years. These were usually entitled "The History of Sir Richard Whittington, thrice Lord Mayor of London, shewing how he came up a poor boy to London, and was received as a scullion boy by a merchant; his sufferings and afflictions under a cruel cook-maid, How he bought a cat for a penny, and sent her a venture beyond sea, for which he got great riches in exchange. And lastly, how he married his Master's daughter, and was made thrice Lord Mayor of London."

This account was published in some shape early in the seventeenth century as reference is made to it in 1605, and it is alluded to later. In 1739 an opera on the subject was produced. Some antiquarians have stated that it was founded upon an Oriental tale. It is related in a Persian manuscript that in the tenth century the son of a poor widow embarked for India, with a cat, his entire property, and that he fortunately arrived at a time the palace was overrun with rats or mice. Additional early references to its popularity might be recorded as well as other stories similar to the legend of Whittington and his cat, and it is difficult to explain why the life of Whittington was chosen as the framework of this folk-tale. It appeared in ballad form about 1640, and in 1668 Pepys saw a puppet show of Whittington at the Southwark Fair.

"The Renowned History of Valentine and Orson, the two sons of the Emperor of Greece, newly corrected and amended. Adorn'd with Cuts," another popular chapbook, was published at Lyon in 1495, as a romance, and in 1558 an edition was printed in Italian at Venice. According to Halliwell, the incident of the wooden horse was taken from "L'Histoire de Clamades et Clarmonde," printed at Lyon in 1488 and in 1586 Thomas Purfoot had a license to print "the old booke of Valentine and Orson." This French romance was very popular for a long period of time.

"The Right Pleasant, and Variable Trachical History of Fortunatus, where by a young man may learn how to behave himself in all worldly affairs and casual chances. First penned in the Dutch tongue, there-hence abstracted, and now first of all published in English by T. C. London, printed by T. B. for Hanna Sawbridge, at the sign of the Bible on Ludgate-hill, near Fleetbridge, 1682." This is a black letter chapbook illustrated by woodcuts probably obtained in Holland or Germany where the art of book illustration was important. The particular cuts in this edition are not uniformly good nor are they all by the same hand, according to Halliwell and the better cuts may have been the work of Jost Amman. "Fortunatus" was without doubt printed before 1600. The story is mentioned in different works that were printed in 1577 and 1602.

Figure 29

Thomas Hickathrift exhibiting his great strength.

"The History of Guy, Earl of Warwick," a favorite Aldermary Church Yard chapbook that circulated in other editions as early as 1706, is a story of love and of valour. "In the blessed time when Athelstone wore the crown of the English na-[ti]r Guy (Warwick's mirror, and all the world's wonder) was the chief hero of the [da]y was also in love with "Phillis the fair, whose beauty and virtue were ines-[timable] shining with such heavenly lustre that Guy's poor heart was ravished in adora-[tion]. Phillis, however, being the daughter and heiress of the Earl of Warwick at first r[efused] Guy, saying "You are but young and meanly born, and unfit for my degree," but l[ove ha]d pierced her heart with a powerful dart and she told him to engage in bold ac[tion]s and noble actions as broad and glorious as the sun and then his suit could no[t be refus]ed. So he armed himself like a knight and crossed the raging ocean arriving at [the cour]t of Thrace, where he won the emperor's daughter by engaging in combat with seve[ral Pri]nces. "Guy laid about him like a lion, among the Princes; here lay one head-less, another without a leg or an arm, and there a horse. Guy still like Hercules, charged desperately, and killed a German prince and his horse under him." However, he did not take the emperor's daughter, but returned to England for Phillis and sad to re-late, that lady said to him, "I have heard of thy winning the Lady Blanch from royal Dukes and Princes, and I am glad to find that Guy is so victorious. But indeed Guy thou must seek more adventures." And Guy, discomfited, went forth again and slaughtered 30,000 men in two battles, in addition to two dragons and a ferocious boar. Upon his return to England this time, he married Phillis and shortly after, her father died, leaving all his estate to Guy and the King made him Earl of Warwick.

At the pinnacle of his glory, he became conscience stricken because of his form-er sins and of his youthful time spent with women and he left his wife to make a pil-grimage to the Holy Land for the health of his soul. Phillis was sad but did not oppose him. On this trip Guy killed a mighty giant and took up the cause of the Earl of Terry whose enemy he killed. After killing one more giant, Guy went into the fields and lived very pensively and alone in a cave. When his end was near he sent a messenger to Phil-lis, "at the sight of which she hastened to her Lord, where with weeping joy they em-braced each other. Guy departed this life in her arms, and was honourably interred. His widow grieving at his death, died fiften days after him."

Some of the early Guy of Warwick chapbook accounts were derived from Samuel Rowlands' "Famous History of Guy Earle of Warwick" which was printed nine times between 1600 and 1700. A comparison of the chapbook text with the text of Rowlands' poem shows that the chapbook account was derived from the poem by some one who excluded every trace of rhyme but who did not object to the presence of metre.

The tale of Cinderella, her unkind stepmother, the jealous sisters, and the recognition of Cinderella by her slipper, is too well known for repetition. In 1893 there was published in London for the Folk-Lore Society, a work by Marian R. Cox en-titled "Cinderella, Three Hundred and Forty-five Variants." This book shows the dif-fusion of the Cinderella story over Europe, Asia, Africa and America. Andrew Lang be-lieved that the diffusion of tales was possible and conceivable, and also that similar institutions and similar imaginative conditions might give rise to similarities in tales in countries that were not in "culture contact" with each other.

There were prose versions of "The Whole Life and Merry Exploits of Bold Robin Hood," of "The History of the Life and Death of that Noble Knight Sir Bevis of South-ampton," abridged from the romance, of "The History of the Sleeping Beauty in the Wood," of "The Life and Death of St. George, The Noble Champion of England," of the "Two Chil-dren in the Wood," of "Bluebeard," of "The History of Fair Rosamond," of King Arthur and of lesser characters such as "The famous history of Johnny Armstrong of Westmore-land," "The famous history of the valiant London 'prentice," "The History of Sinbad the sailor" of Jane Shore, etc.

Thomas Richardson of Derby brought out Jane Shore embellished with a brightly colored folding frontispiece, under the fascinating title, "The affecting history of Jane Shore, the wife of a London merchant, who was seduced by King Edward IV King of

England, recounting Her Splendid Living During the Life of her Royal Lover, The Severe Penance she underwent, the desertion of her friends, Her Subsequent Wretchedness, and Dreadful Death in the open fields, by order of King Richard the Third, otherwise Crooked-Back Dick."

Jane, the only child of a London mercer was brought up with tenderness and indulgence and was educated in ornamental accomplishments such as music, singing, dancing. Her father's trade was among the court ladies and through them Jane was finally introduced into the best companies. "The gracefulness of her mien, and the sweetness of her beauty, drew the eyes and notice of all the men upon her." Eventually she married Mr. Matthew Shore, a goldsmith, and "each day beheld her rising in fresh glory, decked with all the profusion of jewels and other ornaments that an amorous and over-fond husband could bestow, to improve and set off her native perfections." Lord Hastings, a former unsuccessful suitor, now appears as a visitor to the Shore household, and tries again without success to take her by storm. Failing in this, Hastings out of revenge tells the king of Mrs. Shore's wit and accomplishments, hoping that after becoming a favorite of the King, Mrs. Shore might be less obstinate toward his solicitations. King Edward, disguised as a merchant, goes to Mr. Shore's home and although he met with little success with Mrs. Shore, when she found out that he was the king, she left her husband and was installed in a little place not far from the palace. "From the first hour the king received her into his arms, she held the chief place in his affections all the remaining part of his life."

"But when the fatal day was, in which King Edward ended his reign and life together, his beloved mistress was cast out of her paradise, and fell from the summit of her exalted station. It was an easy descent at first from the crown to the coronet; from the bed of majesty to that of high nobility." The eldest son of King Edward, being too young to hold the reins of empire, the Duke of Gloucester was made protector of the realms. Internal politics resulted in Hastings losing his head and in Mrs. Shore being charged with witchcraft, and turned over to the spiritual court for correction. "Stript of all her ornaments and covered with a white sheet, bare legged, and the sharp stones wounding her tender feet, she was brought by way of procession, with the cross carried before her, and a wax taper in her hand, from the Bishop of London's palace to St. Paul's, through crowds of rabble, who flocked to gaze on her. Being placed in the choir, directly opposite the preacher, she, in a set form of words, declared her enormities and her repentence of them."

"Tradition goes farther with her misfortunes, and carries them to a height most terrible, and horrid even to mention; that the tyrant Richard put out a proclamation, commanding all people, upon pain of death and confiscation of goods, not to harbour her in their houses, or relieve her with food or raiment. Thus, the miserable Jane wandered from one place to another." And it is uncertain where and in what manner her life ended, even though some chapbooks claim that it was the gutter.

Chapter 14

OF DRAMATIC CHAPBOOKS

Comparatively few in number, the dramatic chapbooks include such titles as "Cupid & Psyche; a pantomine now in representation at Paris," London; "As you like it; a comedy. As it is acted at the Theatres-royal in Drury Lane and Covent-Garden. By William Shakespear. London, 1777;" "The Gentle Shepherd; a Scots pastoral comedy. By Allan Ramsay. With all the songs, Falkirk, 1782;" "The Tempest; a comedy. Written by William Shakespeare. Taken from the manager's book at the Theatre royal, Drury-Lane, London; and others involving such plays as "The cheats of Scapin," "Comus; a masque," "Ducks and green peas," "The soldier's return," "The Thespian Oracle," etc.

In the chapbook published by M. Angus and Son of Newcastle, entitled "Ducks and Green Peas; or, the Newcastle Rider: a Farce of one act founded in Fact," eight of its twenty-four pages are taken up with the metrical tale "The Newcastle Rider, upon which the farce is probably founded.

"Ducks and Green Peas" is somewhat amusing to read and no doubt was more so when acted. The first scene is laid in a low room in the Queen's Head. Lord Joseph enters and boisterously refuses to have anything to do with anyone except the landlord, to whom he gives orders for an upper room and a meal of two ducks and a peck of green peas. The second scene is in the kitchen where two waiters discuss Lord Joseph. One waiter says, "A very strange fellow this that's just alighted, I warrant he's some upstart or another, flush of money for the present, and consequently flush of pride.--However, I shall pay him the less respect for those fine airs he gives himself." The fourth scene shows Mr. and Mrs. Manley entering the hotel and the landlord tells them about Lord Joseph and his order, whereupon Mr. Manley suggests that he and his wife would like to sup with him. In the fourth scene Joseph is lolling upon a settle, singing. When the landlord makes the suggestion of his two new guests, Joseph replies, "Sup with me, quotha--hold you there,--as I stopped here with a full intention to indulge my appetite for once, I will admit of no interlopers, by Jupiter; a couple too!--I thank you Mr. Boniface, for your damn'd complimentary message; zoons, I should not have so much as a rump, perhaps, for myself, if they are half as hungry as I am--no, no by this hat I'll take care of number one--Let me see, I fancy I shall lay in the next room, I'll see what sort of a bed there is."

In the fifth scene Mr. and Mrs. Manley are seated in the garden where the landlord tells them how Joseph had received their suggestions. Mr. Manley then suggests that as Mrs. Manley is very hungry perhaps Joseph may allow her alone to partake of his supper. In the sixth scene a table is spread in the blue chamber. And the landlord's second suggestion is received by Joseph as follows: "I thought I had satisfied you sufficiently before. Dem you, d'ye mean downright to affront me,--either get along about your business, send up some supper immediately, or I'll kick you down stairs, leave your damn'd troublesome house, and never set my foot in it again, for I tell you positively for the last time, was she the queen herself, she should not sup with me, you scoundrel."

The seventh scene is in the parlor, where the landlord and Mr. and Mrs. Manley are talking over the latest developments. Mr. Manley is anxious to see what kind of a chap Joseph is and it is decided that he is to follow the landlord up to Joseph's room. In the last scene Joseph is singing a song when the landlord enters to tell him that his supper is coming up. Mr. Manley then appears and is immediately recognized by Joseph as his master whereupon Joseph is greatly embarrassed and apologetic. And everything ends by all three sitting down at the meal of ducks and green peas.

On the cover page of "The Wanderer: or the Rights of Hospitality, An Historical Drama. As it is performed at Covent-Garden Theatre," published by J. Scales of London, there are advertised the following "Melo-Dramas, Forty Thieves--Wood Dæmon--Ella Rosenberg--Blind Boy--Harlequin in his Element, &c."

Some of the dramatic chapbooks had colored frontispieces, and there were certain publishers who specialized in plays. These plays, for the most part, were no doubt purchased by persons interested in the theatre and it was not until collectors became interested in them that they were classified as chapbooks. John Cumberland of 19 Ludgate Hill, London, was one of such specialists and among other plays, he published John Howard Payne's "Two Galley Slaves" and "Charles the Second," both having frontispieces drawn by R. Cruikshank. Collectors of literature of the early theatre no doubt have many dramatic pamphlets that collectors would classify as chapbooks.

"The Theatrical Speaker. A selection of the newest and most popular Recitations of the present day," was printed as late as 1840 by Caldwell and Son, of Paisley. This is a twenty-four-page chapbook containing various recitations, including such pieces as "The County Schoolmaster," "Alonzo the Brave," "On the Downfall of Poland," and "The Drunkard and His Bottle."

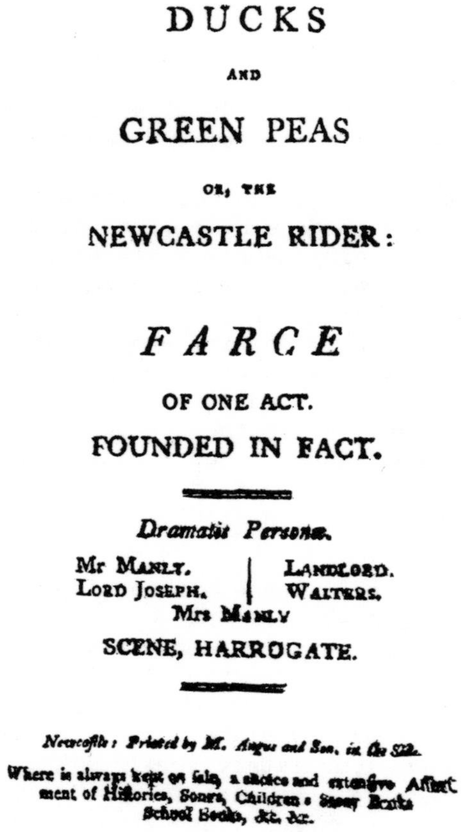

DUCKS

AND

GREEN PEAS

OR, THE

NEWCASTLE RIDER:

FARCE

OF ONE ACT.

FOUNDED IN FACT.

Dramatis Personæ.

Mr MANLY. | LANDLORD.
LORD JOSEPH. | WAITERS.
Mrs MANLY

SCENE, HARROGATE.

Newcastle: Printed by M. Angus and Son, in the Side.

Where is always kept on sale, a choice and extensive Assortment of Histories, Songs, Children's Story Books, School Books, &c. &c.

Figure 30

"Ducks and Green Peas, A Farce."

Chapter 15

OF METRICAL TALES AND OTHER VERSE IN CHAPBOOKS

Many of the legendary, prose tales that appeared in some chapbooks, also appeared in others in metre, and in addition there were many other chapbooks carrying other metrical tales and verse, making this group a fairly large one. "The babes in the wood," "The battle of the Boyn," "The Berkshire Tragedy," "The bride's burial," "The duke of Argyle's courtship," "The duke of Gordon's three daughters," "Jemmy & Nancy of Yarmouth," "The merchant of Bristol's daughter," "The Plymouth tragedy," "The rakish husband," "Robin Hood," "Sweet William of Plymouth," etc., as well as many garlands, appeared in metrical form in various chapbooks.

James Hodges of London, published "Robin Hood's Garland, being a compleat history of all the notable and merry exploits perform'd by him and his men on divers occasions. To which is added three original songs, which has not been printed in any edition for upwards of an hundred years." This is a ninety-six page chapbook, with a woodcut frontispiece.

Robin Hood was born in Nottingham county during the reign of Henry II, about 1160, and in his youth he is reported to have been extravagant and wild, so much so that his inheritance was exhausted and he was outlawed for debt. In view of this he sought refuge in the forests where he was joined by other persons in similar circumstances. With Robin Hood as their leader, his company, consisting of a hundred archers, was always at war with the king of England and all his subjects, except the poor and needy. They lived in the forests and what was not supplied by nature, they took from rich travellers, and Robin Hood eventually became known as a most celebrated robber. He reigned supreme, defied the magistrates and died principally from the infirmities of old age on November 18, 1247. Because he displayed a spirit of freedom and independence in a barbarous age and under tyranny, he was greatly admired by the common people and his life and exploits were made the subject of numerous poems, songs and ballads. In 1795 Mr. Joseph Ritson published a collection of them, and in 1832 the number was added to and a second edition was published in London entitled "Robin Hood: A Collection of all the ancient Poems, Songs, and Ballads, now extant relative to that celebrated English Outlaw. To which are prefixed Historical Anecdotes of his Life. By Joseph Ritson." Robin Hood was not such a favorite with chapbook publishers as one might suppose, probably on account of the difficulty of confining his adventures to twenty-four pages. Nevertheless, he did appear in some chapbooks with his exploits greatly abbreviated.

In the chapbooks, "The History of Adam Bell, Clim of the Clough, and William of Cloudeslie," the account follows the old poem closely. The three men were outlaws and William of Cloudeslie, being married, longed to see his wife and children at Carlisle. When he arrived there, an old woman, whom he had charitably kept for seven years and more, betrayed him to the sheriff. His house was surrounded and set on fire, and after he had helped his family out of a back window, he was forced to come out and be captured and was sentenced to be hanged the next day. Adam Bell and Clim heard of it and went to Carlisle and rescued him after killing the justice, sheriff and hundreds of citizens. William's wife joined them and they travelled to London to ask the king for a pardon. At first he refused but the queen persuaded him to grant it, which he did, just before a message from Carlisle arrived advising him of their dreadful doings. It was too late to recall the pardon, but the king said that unless they defeated his archers they would die. William was successful in this as he split a hazel wand at four hundred paces and shot an apple off his son's head at one-hundred and twenty paces. The king was so amazed that he said:

Now God forbid, then said the King,
That thou should shoot at me.
I give thee Eighteen pence a Day,
And my Bow shalt thou bear,
Yea, over all the North Country,
I make thee Chief Keeper.
Ill give thee Thirteen pence a Day.

And the queen made him gentleman of clothing, his son a cellarist and his wife, chief gentlewoman to govern her nursery. Sometimes this tale was adorned by cuts that had originally appeared in "Robin Hood's Garland," but chapbook readers, as far as is known, never objected to this.

A popular chapbook ballad in this group of metrical tales was "The Battle of Chevy Chase," sometimes entitled "The Famous and Memorable History of Chevy Chace by the River Tweed in Scotland." Therein is recounted the dispute between Earl Percy and Earl Douglas over the hunting in Chevy Chase, how their followers fought and finally:

At last these two stout Earls did meet,
Like captains of great might;
Like lions mov'd they laid on blows,
And made a bloody fight.

Figure 31

Title page illustration from
"The History of Adam Bell, Clim of the
Clough, and William of Cloudeslie."

Finally Earl Douglas was killed by an English arrow and Earl Percy was killed by a Scottish spear. The fight went on and

Of twenty-hundred Scottish spears,
   Scarce fifty-five did fly,
Of fifteen hundred Englishmen
   Went home but fifty-three.

In "Watty & Meg; or, the Wife Reformed," Watty's wife Meg has a terrible temper, and in discussing his unhappiness in local tavern, Watty is advised to threaten her with desertion. During the course of

Figure 32

"Watty & Meg."

this advice, Meg makes her appearance and starts to scold Watty.

> Nasty gude-for-naething being!
> O ye snuffy drucken sow!
> Bringan wife and weans to ruin,
> Drinkin' here wi' sic a crew!
>
> Rise! ye drucken beast o' Bethel!
> Drink's your night and day's desire
> Rise this precious hour, or faith I'll
> Fling your whisky i' the fire.

Watty endured this and more, and went home with Meg bringing up the rear, and arousing the neighborhood with her noise and cursing. Watty kept silent all evening and in the morning he threatened to leave her.

> Fareweel, Meg! - And O! may heav'n
> Keep you aye within his care;
> Watty's heart ye've lang been grievin',
> Now he'll never fash you mair.

After more in this vein -

> Mag a' sabbin, sae to lose him,
> Sic a change had never wist,
> Held his haun close to her bosom,
> While her heart was like to burst.

Meg promises to be good but Watty is not softened at first and reminds her of previous promises that she has broken. However in the end, after Meg promises never to scold him again, never to seek him in the tavern, never to scowl at him when he comes home, never to kick his shins and pull his hair, and to allow him to keep the money, Watty stays.

Another metrical chapbook favorite was "The Constant Lovers; or Tragical Loves of Jemmy & Nancy of Yarmouth."

> Lovers, I pray, lend an ear to my story,
> Take an example by this constant pair;
> How love a young virgin did blast in her glory,
> Beautiful Nancy of Yarmouth we hear.

Nancy, a merchant's only daughter, was courted by the son of gentleman who lived nearby but her parents looked upon him with disfavor.

> Daughter, they said, give o'er your proceeding;
> If that against our consent you do wed,
> For evermore we resolve to disown you,
> If you wed with one that is so mean bred.

Nancy insisted on remaining true to Jemmy, and her father said that if Jemmy would take an ocean trip in one of his ships, he could have Nancy upon his return to Yarmouth. But the cruel father arranged for the murder of Jemmy, whose ghost appeared before Nancy and told her what had happened, whereupon Nancy joined her dead lover by jumping into the sea, although the chapbook account persists in calling it "the deep."

After two or three days these unfortunate lovers were seen, in each other's arms, floating by the side of a ship on the watery main and the boatswain, who had pushed Jemmy overboard to his death, was overcome with remorse and confessed.

> On board the ship he was tried for murder,
> At the yard's arm was hanged for the same,
> Her father he soon broke his heart for his daughter,
> Before the ship into the harbour then came.

Courtship, betrayed damsels, drowned lovers, tragedies, cupid's conquests, and similar subjects seem to prevail in the contents of the metrical tales and verses found in chapbooks. In "The Berkshire Lady's Garland," there are shown in four parts, "Cupid's Conquest over a coy Lady of five-thousand a-year, &c.; The Lady's letter of a challenge to fight him upon refusing to wed her in a mask without knowing who she was; How they met by appointment in a Grove, where she obliged him to fight or wed her; How they rode together in her gilded Coach to her Noble Seat or Castle, &c."

And in "Rosanna; The Oxford Tragedy. In two parts," part I deals with "How Fair Rosanna, of the City of Oxford, was by a young Gentleman betrayed of her virginity" and part II with "His cruelty in murdering her, and how a rose-bush sprung upon her grave, which blossoms all the year through; and how the murder came to be found out, by his cropping the rose, &c." For the benefit of those who are curious about the way the murderer was discovered, we shall allow the poem to speak for itself.

> If any one did crop that rose
> In a moment it would grow again;
> This thing was blaz'd the country round,
> And thousands went the same to see.
>
> He amongst the rest must curious be,
> To go and see if it was true,
> And when unto the place he came,
> The beauteous rose he saw in bloom.
>
> The leaves did fall from off the bush,
> The rose within his hand did die;
> He cried, 'tis fair Rosanna's blood,
> That did spring from her fair body.
>
> Many people that were there,
> Took notice of what he did say,
> They told he had some murder done,
> He the truth confess'd without delay.
>
> They dug and found the body there,
> The first of April it was known,
> He was seiz'd and carried off to jail,
> And shortly after suffer'd his doom."

In "The Bloody Gardener's Tragedy," another favorite, a shepherd's daughter, of beauty bright, both fair and clear, was courted by a noble lord, whose parents, of course, opposed the match, and had a charming girl already picked out for him. But the lord was adamant for his own choice, whereupon the lord's mother conspired with her gardner, to whom she gave eighty pounds, to murder the shepherd's daughter and bury her body. The next day the lord missed his shepherdess and while he was lamenting, the birds around him kept saying that his true love had gone and a milk-white dove hovered on his breast. He returned to his mother and told her what had happened and that he suspected her of killing his sweetheart.

> His mother hearing of what he did say,
> Did turn as pale as death, and swoon'd away:
>   She in distraction run,
>   And told him what she'd done,
> And where the virgin's body it was laid.

The lord then "took a knife and pierced his body through and the lovers in one silent tomb were laid."

"The Jolly Beggar," also a favorite with chapbook publishers and I suppose readers as well, is a rather rowdy account of a beggar's experience with a lassie

> There was a jolly beggar, and a beggin he was bound,
> And he took up his quarters into a lan'art town
> > Fa la, la, &c.
> He wad neither ly in barn, nor yet wad he in byre,
> But in ahint the ha' door, or else afore the fire.
>
> Up raise the goodman's dochter, and for to bar the door,
> And there she saw the beggar standing i' the floor.
> He took the lassie in his arms and to the bed he ran,
> O hooly, hooly wi' me, Sir, ye'll waken our good man."

And so on in the same vein.

"The Death and Burial of Cock Robin" is too well known to quote, but it too was a favorite in the children's chapbooks issued by Catnach, Fortey, William Walker and Sons, and other publishers. Frequently its crude illustrations were brightly and fearfully colored by hand, and it was further adorned by thin, colored paper covers. Other metrical tales for children appeared in a similar style.

A Dublin chapbook, "Sold at the Wholesale and Retail School Book Warehouse, 3 Mary-street" is entitled "The Dublin Tragedy, Or the Unfortunate Merchant's Daughter, in two parts." Part I sets forth, "a brief and authentic account of a rich Merchant's Daughter in the town of Belfast, who was deluded by an Ensign in the army, and for love of him, dressed herself in man's apparel, and sailed with him to England, and were married at Stratford." Part II describes, "How she bought a Lieutenant's Commission for him and became an Ensign herself and soon after went to America: also giving an account of their hardships whilst in an American prison, shewing how after their return to Ireland, she was slighted by her false lover, and afterwards poisoned herself for his sake."

"The Laidley Worm, Of Spindleston Heugh, a song above 500 years old, composed by the Old Mountain Bard, Duncan Frasier, living on Cheviot, A.D. 1270," frequently appeared in chapbooks. It begins:

> The king is gone from Bambrough castle,
> Long may the princess mourn;
> Long may she stand on the castle wall,
> Looking for his return.

Finally the king returns with a queen and all the lords in the country are there to welcome them. The queen, because of the great beauty of the princess, her stepdaughter, is envious of her and says

> I will her liken to a Laidley worm,
> That wraps about the stone,
> And not till Childe Wynd comes back,
> Shall she again be won.
>
> The princess stood at the bower door
> Laughing,--who could her blame?
> But ere the next day's sun went down,
> A long worm she became.
>
> For seven miles east, and seven miles west,
> And seven miles north and south,
> No blade of grass or corn would grow,
> So venomous was her mouth.

This worm drank the milk of seven stately cows, each day before she went to sleep. Finally word went over the sea and the Child of Wynd got word of it. Calling his thirty merry men together, he told them that he wanted to go to Spindleston to see the worm and that he feared something must ail his only sister Margaret. And so a ship was built and in spite of the spells of the queen's witch wives and of the efforts of

armed men, it managed to get to the beach at Spindleston and the Child reached the shore
safely. Running to the worm -

> And now he drew his berry broad sword,
> And laid it on her head,
> And swore if she did harm to him
> That he would strike her dead.
>
> O! quit thy sword, and bend thy bow,
> And give me kisses three;
> For though I am a poisonous worm,
> No hurt I'll do to thee.

This was done and the worm crept into a hole and stepped out a lady, minus
clothing, but she was wrapped in a mantle and taken to Bambrough castle.

> The queen they wanted, whom they found
> All pale and sore afraid;
> Because they knew her power must yield
> To Child Wynd's, who said
>
> Woe be to thee! thou wicked witch,
> An ill death may thou dee
> As thou my sister has likened,
> So liken'd shalt thou be.

And so the queen was turned into a toad.

> Now on the sand, near Ida's tower,
> She crawls a loathsome toad,
> And venom spits on every maid
> She meets upon her road.

Some of the metrical accounts deal with murder, as well as with love and witchcraft. J. Evans of Long-Lane, London, brought out "The Glocestershire Tragedy, Being an
Account of Miss Mary Smith, in Thornbury, Who Poisoned her Father Sir John Smith, For
Love of a young Man." The title page also announces "With an Account of her Trial, and
Dying Speech, at the Place of Execution, which was in Gloucester Market Place at the
last Assizes. You have also the Text of her Funeral Sermon, which was preached the Morning before her Execution.....Also, an Account how the young Man died for Grief, &c."

Chapter 16

OF CHAPBOOKS CONTAINING SONGS

These were so numerous that they far outnumbered other types of chapbooks and the songs that were printed seem innumerable. The song chapbooks were preceded, of course, by the ballad sheets or broadsides. Later, sheets of the same size carried printing on both sides and were folded into 4, 8, 16, etc. pages, becoming chapbooks. Ballads were popular and came in with printing, and were used for educational and political, as well as amusement purposes. Many ballad sheets were printed in black letter long after this form of type had been discarded, and this practice continued to the end of the seventeenth century, making some of them look older than they really are. The use of woodcuts, which ornamented the ballad sheets, was transferred to the chapbooks and they usually appeared on the title page. However, we are here concerned only with the chapbook "songsters" as they are sometimes called. The garlands were usually ballad sheets, each folded twice and varied in size from about 6 x 4 inches to 7 x 5 inches. The front page carried a woodcut and a list of the songs. Some of the sixteenth and seventeenth century garlands carried such poetic titles as "A Handful of Pleasant Delites," "The Garland of Loyalty," and "The Crown Garland of Goulden Roses." At this period they ran to twenty or thirty pages.

As the eighteenth century arrived they were confined to four pages, or a single sheet folded twice, then they grew to eight pages and some of the more elaborate ones had twenty-four or more pages and sometimes a colored frontispiece. Music was never printed, but in many cases, the song was directed to be sung to a certain tune. Later, even this disappeared.

In many cases, the names given to the garlands are quite amusing. There were garlands for fond mothers, frolicksome ladies, happy couples, a hungry man, a jolly sailor, lovely Jenny, the parson, the meal-monger, the old maid, the fashionable dandy, a smirking lass, the unfortunate weaver, the willing bachelor, the rake, the reaper, as well as "The Maidenhead's Garland," "The Duke of York's Garland," "The Pink Garland," "The Cuckold's Cap Garland," "The Greenland Fisherman's Garland," and "The Greenwich lover's Garland."

In 1686, T. Passenger at the Three Bibles, on London Bridge, London, brought out "The Loyal Garland, as a choice collection of songs, highly in request, and much esteemed in the past and present times; made by diverse ingenious persons, on sundry occasions, for the sake of merryment. And sung with great applause, as being the flower of collection and rarity." This is in black-letter and contains eighty-three songs and ballads, including "Loyelty turn'd up Trump, or the danger over," "The Loyalists Incouragement," and others that have nothing to do with loyalty.

"Mad Tom's Garland, composed of six excellent songs "reminds one of King Lear" and Poor Tom.

> I am old Mad Tom, behold me,
> I am old Mad Tom, behold me,
> And my wits are quite fled from me!
> I am made I am sure, I am past all cure
>   Yet I hope to be reclaimed.

In "The Sailor's Songster," printed by J. Marshall of Newcastle all the titles seem to have something to do with, or some connection with the life of a sailor. Some of the songs are "The Tempest," "The Old Commodore," "The Sea Boy," "The Jolly Tar," "Heaving of the Lead," "Poor Joe the Marine" and "The Battle of the Nile."

In "An Excellent Garland; Containing four new Songs," printed at Congleton by
J. Dean, one is entitled "The Joys of the Bottle," and starts off as follows:

> While nostrums are held out to cure each disease,
> And to parry with death or with pain as we please,
> The protractor of life and preserver of ease
>   I have ever yet found in a bottle.
>
> For when care like a clog hangs about my poor heart,
> And health from the burden seems bent to depart,
> I the millstone shake off, and death draws back his dart,
>   When he sees that my doctor's a bottle.

In "The Bouquet; Composed of three-and-twenty favorite new songs" published at
Derby in 1793, there is one called "Description of London," which makes fun of the dress
of that period:

> Nay the ladies, I vow,
> I cannot tell how,
> Were now white as a curd, & now red
>   La! how would you stare
>   At their huge crop of hair,
> Tis a hay-cock o' top of their head!

J. Marshall of Newcastle issued many eight-page chapbooks each containing from
four to six songs, with a woodcut on the cover. These were usually called "A Garland
of New Songs," and contained songs of lovers, merchants, sailors, various happenings,
etc. Some of the titles are "Paddy O'Leary," "I was the Boy for bewitching 'em." "Death
of Liberty," "The Woodpecker," "Black-ey'd Susan," "The Bewildered Maid," "The Constant
Shepherd," "The Tinker," "Robin Adair," "Dear Maid I love thee," etc. One of these
called "Sally Roy" starts off as follows:

> Fair Salley, once the village pride,
> Lies cold and wan in yonder valley;
> She lost her lover, and she died;
> Grief broke the heart of gentle Sally.
> Young Valiant was the hero's name,
> For early valour fir'd the boy,
> Who barter'd all his love for fame;
> And kill'd the hopes of Sally Roy.

Some song chapbooks had no particular title. The name of the first song was
printed in large type on the cover, followed by the words "To which are added," in turn
followed by the names of the three or four songs, as for example "Bonny Mally Stewart;
To which are added, "Her blue rollin' e'e. The braes o' Gleniffer. Waes me for prince
Charly. Stirling. Printed by W. Macnie, 1825." "Her Blue Rollin' E'e" begins -

> My lassie is lovely at May-dew adorning,
> Wi' gowans and primroses ilka green lea,
> Tho' sweet is the violet new blown in the morning,
> As tender and sweet is her blue rollin' ee.

There were many songs for and against whisky. One called "Effects of Whisky
begins as follows and continues in the same vein:

> Whisky makes us sometimes foolish,
> Whisky makes our pockets light,
> Whisky makes us aften mulish,
> Whisky gars us aften fight.
>
> Whisky sometimes cures the head-ache,
> Whisky aften cures the gripes,
> Whisky aye can cure the tooth-ache,
> Whisky's gude when ta'en wi' swipes.

Many chapbooks were headed "Two Popular Songs," "Four Excellent New Songs," "Six Excellent New Songs," "Seven Popular Songs," etc., with the word Songs in very large type. Many of these were printed at Falkirk, and included "Falkirk Muir," "Falkirk Fair," "Highland Widow's Lament," "Farewell my Dame," "Tweed Side," "The Last Rose of Summer," "The White Cockade," etc., the first two verses of the latter being as follows:

> My love was born in Aberdeen,
> The bonniest lad that e'er was seen,
> But now he makes our hearts fu' sad,
> He's ta'en the field wi' his white cockade.
>
> O he's a ranting roving blade!
> O he's a brisk and boony lad!
> Betide what may my heart is glad,
> To see my lad wi' his white cockade.

A
GARLAND
OF
NEW SONGS.

Paddy Carey
Battle of the Nile
Nancy's Journal
The Galley Slave

Newcastle-upon-Tyne:
Printed by J. Marshall, in the Old Flesh-Market.
Where may also be had, a large and curious Assortment
of Songs, Ballads, Tales, Histories, &c.

Figure 33

"A Garland of New Songs"

THE
Delights of the
SPRING.

Being a Choice Collection of SONGS,
SUNG at the THEATRES ROYAL; SADLERS-WELLS
VAUXHALL; ROYAL CIRCUS; ASTLEY'S
And all the PUBLIC PLACES of AMUSEMENT.

1. Mary's Dream.	11. I'll take care how I Marry again.
2. O Fresh is the Breeze of the Mountain.	12. Little Mary of the Dee
3. For thou art the joy of my Heart,	13. Forget me Not,
4. Braham's Parody	14. Answer to Quite Politely,
5. 'Tis sweet to hear the Village Bells	15. Life of Giovanni,
6. To the Mountain Away.	16. A Parody on Wallace Bled
7. Poor Eleanor Gray.	17. Bartholomew Fair
8. Sweet Rose of England.	18. The Legacy
9. York you're Wanted	19. Dulce Domum
10. Learned Men	20. My charming young Betsy Girl of my Heart &b

Printed and Sold by J. Pitts, No. 14, Great St. Andrew-street

Figure 34

"The Delights of Spring"

Frequently the chapbooks contained a variety of songs within their pages. Thus we have in a Glasgow, eight-page songster, "Dainty Davie," "Sic a Wife as Willie had," "The Blue-Eyed Lassie," "The Rantin Dog the Daddie o't," "Nothing Like Grog," and "The Red Rose." "Nothing Like Grog," no doubt, was meant for lusty throats.

> A plague on those musty old lubbers
>   Who tell us to fast and to think,
> And patiently bear with life's rubbers,
>   With nothing but water to drink;
> A can of good stuff had they swigg'd it,
> Would soon ay have set them agog;
>   In spite of the rules
>   Of the schools,
>   The old fools
> Would have constantly swigg'd it
> And sworn there was nothing like grog.

Another different example is "The Red Red Rose."

> O my luve is like a red red rose,
>   That's newly sprung in June;
> O my luve is like the melodie
>   That's sweetly play'd in tune.
> As fair art thou, my bonnie lass,
>   So deep in love am I;
> And I will love thee still, my dear,
>   Till a' the seas gang dry.

J. Pitts of Seven Dials, London, issued many songs including collections called "The Delights of the Spring," "The Vauxhall Songster," etc., these being "the newest songs now singing at all the different places of public amusement and in all convivial assemblies." Other publishers issued similar collections that contained from twelve to twenty songs and sold for a penny. Pitts also issued little songsters, containing about a dozen songs, each $3\frac{3}{4}$ by $2\frac{1}{2}$ inches, bound in their colored wrappers, called "The Bullfinch, The Linnet, The Vocalist, The Mill, The Drury Lane Concert," etc., and these were illustrated by small woodcuts.

As has been stated, the number of songs in this group seems endless. There were "Sit ye awhile and tipple a bit," "The beadle of the parish," "Blythe, blythe, an' Merry are we," "The Irish Farmer," "Tak' your auld cloke about ye," "The sailor's return," "The orange and blue," "John Anderson, my Jo." "Roy's Wife of Aldivlloch," "Alice Gray," "Get up and bar the door," "A light heart & a thin pair of breeches," "The Irish smuggler," "The lovely lass of Allan-Down," etc., etc. The latter begins as follows:

> Yestreen I had a pint o'wine
>   a place wher body saw na;
> Yestreen lay on this breast of mine
>   the raven locks o' Anna.
>
> The hungry Jew in wilderness,
>   rejoicing o'er his manna,
> Was naething to my hinny bliss
>   upon the lips o' Anna.
>
> Ye monarchs, tak the east and west
>   frae Indies to Savannah;
> Gie me within my straining grasp
>   the melting form of Anna.

Some of the more ambitious "songsters" selling for sixpence and published by Thomas Richardson of Derby, Orlando Hodgson of London and by various other publishers, had from twenty-four to ninety-two and more pages and were frequently embellished with colored folding frontispieces. These sometimes contained fifty or more songs. "Hodgson's Union Song-Book for 1832," is a collection of popular and favorite songs of all sorts and the frontispiece is of the comic valentine type, similar to many other frontispieces. Thomas Richardon's songster has the following long title on the cover page.

Some cover pages listed the songs. "Richardson's new universal Songster, or Sportsman's Companion for the present year, containing all the Newest and most Approved Popular Songs, Calculated to afford Wit, Fun, and Mirth for Ever; with a large collection of Toasts and Sentiments."

Along from about 1830 to 1850 certain firms in Durham, Glasgow and other places issued such titles as "The Negro Minstrel, The English Minstrel, The Scottish Minstrel, The British Minstrel, The Songster's Jewel," etc., running from sixteen to twenty-four pages, all selling for a penny and containing the usual miscellany of songs. As a rule these appeared on a better grade of paper than previous songsters. As a specimen of the Negro dialect of the songs in "The Negro Minstrel," a few verses from "Coal-Black Rose" are quoted:

> Lubly Rose, Sambo cum,
> Don't you hear de banjo - tum, tum, tum?
> Lubly Rose, Sambo cum,
> Don't you hear de banjo - tum, tum, tum?
> Oh Rose, de coal-black rose.
> I wish I may be burnt if I don't lub Rose.
> Oh Rose, &c.
>
> Dat you Sambo? Yes I cum,
> Don't you hear de banjo - tum, tum, tum?
> Dat you Sambo? Yes I cum,
> Don't you hear de banjo - tum, tum, tum?
> Oh Rose, &c.

THE
VOCALIST,
A CHOICE COLLECTION OF
SONGS
Now Singing at all the Public Places of
AMUSEMENT.

LONDON:
PRINTED BY J. PITTS,
Wholesale Toy & Marble Warehouse,
No. 6, Great St. Andrew Street, Seven Dials.

Figure 35

A toy songster issued by J. Pitts.

THE
BERKSHIRE LADY'S
GARLAND.

IN FOUR PARTS.

I. Cupid's Conquest over a coy Lady of five thousand a-year, &c.
II. The Lady's letter of a challenge to fight him upon refusing to wed her in a mask without knowing who she was.
III. How they met by appointment in a Grove, where she obliged him to fight or wed her.
IV. How they rode together in her gilded Coach to her Noble Seat or Castle, &c.

GLASGOW:
PRINTED FOR THE BOOKSELLERS.
26.

Figure 36

The Berkshire Lady's Garland.

Sometimes the choice lyrics of Burns are found rubbing elbows, in some chapbook, with pieces of doggerel not worth printing. In other cases poems of some merit have been altered beyond recognition. On the other hand some of the best of Scottish minstrelsy was circulated among the people by means of chapbooks, even though the publishers and printers forgot to mention the authors. The songs of Burns, Hogg, Scott, Ramsay, Jean Elliot and others frequently appeared in chapbooks, in fact Burns had a chapbook to himself. G. Caldwell & Co. of Paisley issued one entitled "Burns' Popular Songs."

This brief account barely touches the subject of chapbook songs and their variety, and no attempt has been made to evaluate any of them. Some are good, some are bad. If there were no other sources one could find in some of them traces of the customs and thought of the people during the period of their circulation.

One of the later-day chapmen, John Milne, a poet-peddler of Aberdeenshire, sold his own poems over a large area of the east of Scotland, and Harvey states that his verses frequently were occupied with the incidents of the religious struggle that was climaxed in the Disruption of 1843. John Milne was found at all the fairs and markets, with his literary wares.

Chapter 17

OF CHAPBOOKS CONTAINING JESTS, HUMOROUS FICTION, RIDDLES, ETC.

People have always enjoyed jokes, jests, riddles and humor and consequently chapbooks containing such material were numerous and varied. In many cases the humor was broad and coarse, and of a type not usually found on the printed pages of today. However, some of this chapbook humor has its counterpart in the everyday conversation of many people.

Frequently the humor of one age does not appeal to the senses of a later one, consequently some of the chapbook jests appear either dull or far-fetched at present. On the other hand, some of them are truly humorous. The titles of humorous chapbooks are sometimes more amusing than their contents. In 1786 in London, there was published "The frisky jester; or, A feast of laughter for the comical fellows; being such a collection of wit and humour as far exceed anything of the kind hitherto published, consisting of humorous jests, smart repartees, pleasant stories, funny jokes, comical adventures and entertaining humbugs." This is a chapbook of seventy pages. Then there was "Grinning made easy; or, Funny Dick's unrivalled collection of jests, jokes, bulls, epigrams, &c, with many other descriptions of wit and humour," a twenty-four page chapbook issued at Glasgow and other places. Many chapbooks attributed to Dougal Graham appear in this group, such as "The folly of witless women displayed," "The coalman's courtship," "The whole proceedings of Jockey and Maggy," "The Comical Sayings of Pady from Cork," and "The comical and witty jokes of John Falkirk." In 1797, J. Davenport of London, printed "Laugh and grow fat; or, A cure for melancholy, being a collection of witty sayings, arch waggeries, wonderful observations, anecdotes, &c., &c." in twenty-four pages.

"The surprising adventures, miraculous escapes, and wonderful travels of the renowned Baron Munchausen" also appeared in a very much reduced form in chapbooks. "Merry frolicks; or, The comical cheats of Swalpo, a notorious pick-pocket, and the merry pranks of Roger the clown," was an Aldermary Church Yard title of twenty-four pages, in which the tricks of Roger are laughable, but coarse and vulgar. A very popular title was "The world turned upside-down," especially in the edition intended mostly for children. "The Merry tales of the wise men of Gotham" was an old favorite, also "The history and comical transactions of Lothian Tom." and "The entertaining history of the king and the cobbler."

The old English jest books proper, or those containing various jokes, some of them very old, some stolen or borrowed, are now very rare. They were probably read out of existence. These jest books were frequently named after famous clowns or wits and had nothing to do with the persons in question. In the same manner "Cambridge Jests" was published at Newcastle. Oxford too had its jest book, "Gratiae Ludentes, Jests from the Universitie. By H. L. Oxen," printed by Thomas Cotes for Humphrey Mosley, not in Oxford, but in London, of course. One of its anecdotes is labeled "Of Diogenes. One asking Diogenes the Cynicke what hee would have to take a cuffe on the eare, he answered him a helmet. The same man walking in the fields, and seeing a young man shooting very unskilfully, went and sate downe very neere the mark, some asking him why hee did so, hee answered least peradventure hee should hit mee that shootes."

John Browne, of St. Dunstan's Churchyard in Fleet Street published in 1604 "Pasquil's Jests, Mixed with Mother Bunchs Merriments, Whereunto is added a dozen of Gulles. Pretty and pleasant, to drive away the tediousnesse of a winter evening." Nearly everything is printed in black-letter and the contents are not very funny. The practical and other jokes of one Hobson appeared in 1607 as "The Pleasant Conceites of Old Hobson the Merry Londoner," printed in London for John Wright.

There was also "Tarltons Court witty Jests," printed in 1638 and named for
Richard Tarlton the famous comedian of the time of Elizabeth, but he had nothing to do
with it, and it is said to be full of chestnuts.

The best known jest books are the Joe Miller ones and many chapbook publishers
used his name on their compilations. According to an anonymous author in "The Strand
Magazine" some years ago, Joe Miller, although a comedian, seldom spoke and never
laughed. He could neither read nor write and he learned his parts, that he played successfully at Old Drury Lane, with the help of his wife. After his death, a chapbook
publisher named T. Read, collected a book of jests, and put Miller's name on it for the
sake of giving it popularity. This was in 1739 and later editions were published during
the same year. The title was "Joe Miller's Jests or, the Wits Vade-Mecum," etc. Number
99 in this book will be recognized as being in circulation today in one form or another.
"99. A Lady's Age happening to be questioned, she affirmed, she was but Forty, and
call'd upon a Gentleman that was in Company for his Opinion; Cousin, said she, do you
believe I am in the Right, when I say I am but Forty? I ought not to dispute it, Madam,
reply'd he, for I have heard you say so these ten years." Another example is joke 175.
"175. A certain Noblem---, a Cour---r, in the Beginning of the late Reign, coming out
of the H--se of L--ds, accosts the Duke of B---ham, with How does your Pot boil, my Lord,
these troublesome Times? To which his Grace replied, I never go into my Kitchen, but I
dare say the scum is uppermost."

Figure 37

From "The World Turned Upside Down."

A penny chapbook published as late as 1856 in Glasgow is called "The Scrap Book:
A selection of the best Jokes, Puns, Comic Sayings, Jonathanisms, & c., & c." Its twenty-
four pages are full of the following examples of wit, many being much worse. "Horne
Tooke, being asked by George III whether he played at cards, replied 'I cannot, your
majesty, tell a king from a knave.'"

"We notice the marriage of Mr. Day to Miss Field, which presents this singular
anomaly, that although he won the Field, she gained the Day."

"'Am I not a little pale?' inquired a lady who was rather short and corpulent,
of a crusty old bachelor. 'You look more like a big tub,' was the blunt reply."

"A few days since, a person threw the head of a goose on to the stage of the
Belleville Theatre. Cotru advancing to the front, said, 'Gentlemen, if any one amongst
you has lost his head, do not be uneasy, for I will restore it on the conclusion of the
performance.'"

For the benefit of those who burned with love, but who were incapable of devising their own sentiments, there were various Valentine Writers. Charles Barbier in 1669 published a volume of 126 pages entitled, "Valentines, Questions of Love," etc., which contains some sixty amorous lyrics. A somewhat similar work appeared in England in 1784. This was called "The New English Valentine Writer; or, The High Road to Love." Others were called "The Beauties of Humen," "Cupids Directory," "Cupid's Mirror," "The Gentlemen's Polite Valentine Writer," etc. In London these Valentine Writers were published by such firms as A. Kidwell, J. Walton, Dean & Munday, T. Sabine, Thomas Hughes, etc. during the early years of the nineteenth century.

Figure 38

The duel of the palfries.
From "The World Turned Upside Down."

Figure 39

The mad squire and his fatal hunting.
From "The World Turned Upside Down."

All such publications were not devoted to sweet messages, or sentimental ones. A group called Quizzical Valentine Writers, contained satirical or humorous verses. Some of these were named, "Hymen's Revenge Against Old Maids, Old Bachelors and Impertient Coxcombs," "The Quizzical Valentine Writers," "The Whimsical Valentine Writer," etc. Some contained verses suitable for sending to a policeman, a drunkard, a vixen, a cuckold, an old maid, a fashionable, old hag, etc. And a gentleman would have no touble in selecting something with which to annoy a satirical lady, or a lady could pick out verses suitable for a short gentleman or a rake. "Hymen's Wreath," a tradesman's Valentine Writer embraced doggerel for the use of bakers, shoemakers, weavers, stay-makers, fishmongers, sawyers, turners, carpenters, wheelwrights, shepherds, masons, etc., together with fitting replies.

Many Valentine Writers contained from sixteen to twenty-four pages. Some carried poorly drawn, frightfully colored, humorous frontispieces, or illustrated title pages, or both, and these sold usually for sixpence. One of these sixpence ones, printed by Hodgson & Co., London, entitled "The Gentleman's Love Feast: A New and Complete Original Valentine Writer," includes the following lines as suitable for sending to a cheesemonger:

How now old Scrapings! what is here to do?
Why what a mumps to dream I could love you,
Fool be assured me it would never please,
To sell your addled eggs and rotten cheese;
Of trade, the secrets I've no wish to learn,
How you salt butter into fresh can turn,
How Irish bacon you for Wiltshire pass
Thinking the buyer like yourself an ass;
How you cheat folk when goods are in the scale,
Making the lightest by a sleight prevail,
Yet if advice I might presume to give,
Go mend your weights, try honestly to live;
No, Maggot, no! I am not so supine,
No stinkibus shall be my Valentine.

In the penny Valentine Writers one did not have such a large variety to choose from, but the selections were just as choice. J. Turner of Coventry issued a penny one--"The Complete Valentine Writer containing a Choice Selection with a variety for Trades and Professions." Therein one finds lines suitable for a butcher to send to his sweetheart.

> A Butcher I am
> And thou art my lamb,
> And one whom my rib I would make,
> But if you deny,
> A lost mutton I,
> My life will be surely at stake.
> My sweetheart art thou
> Thy skin is, I vow,
> As white as most delicate veal;
> Say, wilt thou be mine,
> My dear Valentine,
> Oh! be not as hard as my steel.

Depending upon the state of her feelings, the sweetheart could use one or the other of the following answers -

> Dear Sir, to be free,
> Thine only I'll be
> Then banish, dear Sir, all thy grief
> And when I am thine,
> My dear Valentine,
> We will have a good sirloin of beef.
>
> - - -
>
> If I be a lamb,
> Then thou art a ram -
> A ram only fit for my sport,
> Or else thou'rt a calf,
> At whom I must laugh
> So vile your endeavors to court.

And finally one more example -

> Your cheeks they have a saffron tint,
> And what is worse, my dear you squint,
> 'Tis reckon'd an unlucky sign,
> To have a squinting Valentine.
> But as 'tis so what can I do
> But pay my best respects to you,
> Accept them, pray, & there's an end on't,
> You'll hear no more from me depend on't.

In 1708, J. Smith of London printed "The French King's Wedding, or the Royal Frolick; being a pleasant account of the intrigues, comical courtship catterwauling, and surprizing marriage ceremonies of Lewis the XIVth with Madam Maintenon, his late hackney of state. With a list of the names of those that threw the stocking on the wedding-night, and Madam Maintenon's speech to the king. As also, a comical wedding-song sung to his majesty by the famous Monsieur la Grice, to the tune of 'The Dame of Honour.' All of which is sufficiently descriptive in itself.

In "Canterbury Tales, composed for the entertainment of all ingenious young men and maids at their merry meetings; intermixed with pleasant stories, witty jests, etc., very proper for town and country" one finds a collection of jests decorated with wood-cuts. The scenes of the stories are laid mostly in Canterbury and the following is an example of the anecdotes.

"A woman having a new high-crowned hat, resolved for the first time of wearing it to go to church in it. When she entered, they were reading these words (which form part of the Church service), 'Lord have mercy upon us!' The woman, being little accustomed to go to church, thought they was (sic) taking her hat off; so in a rage hollowed, --'Lord have mercy upon us! did you never see a woman's high-crowned hat before?'"

An edition of "The Comical and Witty Jokes of John Falkirk the merry Piper" printed in Edinburgh in 1777, which tales are attributed to the authorship of Dougal Graham, contains the following, as well as other coarse stories:

"A certain old reverend priest, being one night at supper in a gentleman's house; and for one article having eggs, the server of the table, as usual laid a cloath on every ones knee, wherewith to hold their egg in when hot, when supper was over, the priest looking down between his legs, and seeing the white cloath thought it was his shirt-tail: and very slyly stops it into his breeches bite, and bite, which the lady and her maid observed, but was ashamed to challenge him; so home he went with the servet in his breeches, and knew nothing of it till going to bed, when it fell from him, his wife enquired how he came by it, he could not tell, but was surprized how he came to have more bulk in his breeches than formerly, but perceiving the name they sent it back again, the priest pleaded to be excused own'd himself only a thief through ignorance."

"As two maids were coming from the milking of their cows, one of them stepping over a style, fell and spill'd the whole peal full of milk from her head O said she, what will I do, what will I do, O said the other maid, let it go who can help it now, you can make it up again it is not your maidenhead: My maiden-head said she, if it were my maiden-head, I would think nothing of it, many, many a time, I have lost my maiden-head with great pleasure, and got it ay again, it came ay back to its ain place again, but I'll never gather up my milk again."

Another Dougal Graham production, "The Scots Piper's Queries; or John Falkirk's Cariches, made Both Plain and Easy" in a Stirling edition, printed by C. Randall, is full of questions and answers, of which the following are typical.

"Q. What is the hardest dinner that ever a taylor laid his teeth to?
A. His own goose, tho' ever so well boiled or roasted.
Q. Where did Moses go when he was full fifteen years old?
A. Into his sixteenth.
Q. What creature resembles most a drunken piper?
A. A cat when she sips milk; she always sings, and so does a piper when he drinks good ale.
Q. What are the two hardest things to be found, and yet they are both good in their kind?
A. Good women and good small beer.
Q. What did Adam first set in the garden of Eden?
A. His foot.
Q. How will you know the bairns of our towns by all others in the kingdom?
A. By their ill-breeding, and bad manners.
Q. Why is a drawn tooth like a thing that is forgot.
A. Because it is out of one's head."

There are many more in the same vein, in this chapbook, together with some that are too vulgar for reproduction.

"The Comical Tricks of Lothian Tom" by Dougal Graham was quite a favorite chapbook subject and is concerned with the doings of one "Thomas Black of Lothian county, who had a good education, which he received rather awkwardly, and who was wild and mischievous. Tom played some pretty mean tricks, of which the following was not the worst.

"It happened one day that Tom went fishing, and brought home a few small fish, which his grandmother's cat snapt up in the dark. So Tom to have justice of the cat for so doing, catches her, and put her into a little tub, or cog, then sets her adrift in a small mill dam, ordering her to go a fishing for herself; then set two or three dogs upon her, and a most terrible sad fight ensued, as ever was seen on fresh water; for if any of the dogs, when attempted to board her, set up their noses, baudrins came flying to that place, to repulse them with her claws; then the vessel was likely to be overset by the weight of herself, so she had to flee to the other, and finding the same there from thence to the middle, where she sat mewing always turning herself about, combing their noses with her foot. The old woman being informed of the dangerous situation of her dearly beloved cat, came running with a long pole to beat off the dogs and have her ashore. What now, says Tom, if you are going to take part with my enemies, you shall have part of their reward; and gives the old woman such a push that she tumbled into the dam over head and ears, beside her beloved cat, and would undoubtedly have perished in the water had not one of the people who was there looking at the diversion, come to her relief."

Another chapbook somewhat similar to Lothian Tom was "The Merry Exploits of Poor Robin, the Merry Saddler of Walden, Containing Many merry Passages of his Life, of harmless Mirth, to lengthen out pleasure and drive away Melancholy." In this Poor Robin engages in exploits that are either rowdy and of no particular interest, or too vulgar to be retold here.

Figure 40

Events in "The History of the
King and the Cobbler."

Figure 41

Long Meg of Westminster.

"The Entertaining History of the King and the Cobler" of which I have a Nottingham edition before me, was also a widely circulated and reprinted chapbook in two parts of sixteen pages each. It details the habit of King Henry VIII in visiting various watches of the city incognito. On one of such visits he becomes acquainted with a merry cobbler by whom he is much diverted and entertained. As a result he invites the cobbler to pay him a return visit and to ask for Harry Tudor. The cobbler's preparation for the visit, his actual reception and his entertainment in the King's cellar where he discovers Harry Tudor to be the king, and of his promotion to a courtier are set forth at length, and are quite amusing. The second part deals with the cobbler's return to his wife and the comical discourse between them, with the attitude of the queen and Cardinal Wolsey toward the king for being too free with a poor cobbler, with the king taking to himself the title of tanner and the queen disguised as a country maid, with the cobbler and his wife dining with the king and with the king granting the cobbler a plot of land worth 50 pounds per year.

"The Life and Pranks of Long Meg of Westminster" was long a popular chapbook and was printed many times. Long Meg herself was frequently alluded to in early writings and there was even a play about her that was a favorite for several years, beginning with 1595. She appeared in black-letter chapbook style in London as early as 1582. This fictitious personage was of course born of honest and healthy parents in the time of Henry VIII. She looked like a tall man cast in a woman's mould and was noted for her strength and wonderful exploits. Being a lusty wench she boxed people on the ears, and could strike a blow like an ox, was handy with the sword, could "rib roast" a man with a cudgel until he was almost dead, and take care of herself much better than any man. And because she beat the Frenchmen from the walls of Boulogne the king gave her eight pence a day for life. Concerning "the combat she had with a Frenchman before the walls of Boulogne, and what was the issue of the combat," we shall allow the chapbook to speak for itself.

"While the Dauphin's army lay in view before Boulogne, there was a Frenchman that sundry times would as on a bravery come within shot and toss his pike, and so go his way. Long Meg seeing the pride of this Frenchman, desired that a drum might be sent, to signify that there was a common soldier, a young stripling, that would at the push of the pike try a veny [attack] with their champion." This was done and "Meg was ready, and went out and met him, and without any salutations they fell to blows, where there was a long and dangerous combat; but at last Meg overthrew him, and laid him along; when she had done, she pulled out her scimitar and cut off his head; and with that pulling off her burganet, [helmet] she let her hair fall about her ears; whereby the Frenchmen perceived that she was a woman: and thereupon the English without Boulogne gave a great shout; and Meg by a drum sent the Dauphin his soldier's head, and said, an English woman sent it him. Whereupon he commended her much, and sent her an hundred crowns for her valour." So much for Long Meg and her merry pranks.

In the following, supposed to be the best of Dougal Graham's work, next to his "History of the Rebellion," we shall allow the title page to speak for itself. This particular edition was printed at Sitrling, by C. Randall in thirty-two pages. "The whole proceedings of Jockey and Maggy. In five parts. 1. Jockey and Maggy's courtship.....ii. The wonderful works of our John, shewing how he made Janet like an Elshin shaft and got his ain Maggy wi' bairn forby. iii. The wonderful works of our John made manifest before the minister. iv. How Jockey and his mother went away to see his bastard child. v. How Jockey had another child and could not get it baptised until he mounted the stool.....Carefully corrected and revised by the author." Although the title page is a synopsis, it does not give one any idea of the amusing incidents in the text.

"Simple Simon's Misfortunes, or his Wife Margery's outragious Cruelty" was published early in the eighteenth century at least. The chapters are headed, "1. An account of Simon's wedding and how his wife Margery scolded him for putting on his roast-meat cloaths the very next morning after he was married. 2. How she dragg'd him up the chimney in a basket a smoak-drying, wherein they used to dry bacon, which made him look like a red herring. 3. How Simon lost a sack of corn as he was going to the mill to have it ground. 4. How Simon went to market with a basket of eggs, but broke them by the way: also how he was put into the stocks. 5. How Simon's wife cudgell'd him for not bringing home money for his eggs. 6. How Simon lost his wife's pail, and burnt the bottom of her kettle. How Simon's wife sent him to buy two pounds of soap, but going over a bridge, let his money fall into the river: also how a ragman run away with his cloaths."

A popular chapbook, especially in the form evolved for children, was "The World Turned Upside-Down, or the Folly of Man, exemplified in twelve comical relations upon uncommon subjects." This was always illustrated by various cuts showing the world turned upside down, the ox turned farmer, the soldier turned nurse, the ox turned butcher, the horse turned groom, the sun, moon, earth and stars transposed, etc. Such popular drolleries as this were published in Rome in the sixteenth century and the subject is often

found in the literature and in l'imagerie populaire of all European countries. In
France, in the eighteenth century, Le Monde renversé was a popular subject with all the
imagiers. The interpretation of the pictures is so easy that the text is unnecessary.
The usual subjects are presented, the daughter giving the bottle to her mother, the son
showing the father how to read, the man carrying the horse, etc. J. Kendrew of Collier-
gate, York, printed a little, gay, penny chapbook on this subject about 1820, illustrated by twenty-nine woodcuts. The early chapbook account was sometimes a set of dreary
moral essays in verse, and not amusing, as were the changed versions of a later day.

        James Kendrew of York, who published many little, penny sixteen-page chapbooks
for children, had several titles such as "The New Riddle Book for the Amusement and Instruction, of Little Misses and Masters," and "A Collection of Birds Riddles." Each
page contained a woodcut, with the riddle beneath, also the answer. These usually were
about as follows:

                        My body is thin,
                        And has no guts within,
                        I have neither head, face, nor eye;
                            But a tail I have got,
                            As long as - what not,
                        And without any wings I can fly.

The answer to this is - a kite.

                        Without a bridge .or a saddle,
                        Across a thing I ride and straddle,
                        And those I ride, by help of me,
                        Though almost blind are made to see.

The answer - spectacles.

                            My back is bare,
                            My belly thin,
                            My guts are all
                            Without my skin,
                            I'm often scrap'd,
                            But never fill'd
                            As many have
                            Oft times beheld.
                            Four teeth I have,
                            But got no tongue,
                            Yet when I speak,
                            Please old and young;
                            My voice it is
                            A pleasing sound,
                            Which makes them oft
                            To trip it round.

And the answer, if it has not be guessed already, is - a violin.

        "The Merry Tales of the Wise Men of Gotham" was a popular and much printed chap-
book, and supposedly the work of Andrew Borde or Boarde, who lived during the fifteenth
and sixteenth centuries. It exists in black-letter and later editions, the following
extract having been taken from an Aldermary Church Yard chapbook.

        "A young man of Gotham went a wooing a fair maid; his master warned him before
hand, whenever you look at her, cast a sheep's eye at her and say "How dost thou do my
sweet pigsnie! The fellow went to the butchers shop and bought seven or eight sheeps
eys; and then when this lusty wooer was at dinner, he would look upon his fair wench,
and cast in her face a sheep's eye saying how do you do, my sweet pigsnie? How do you
do, swine's face? said the wench; what do you mean by casting a sheep's eye at me? O

sweet pigsnie, have at thee another. But I defy thee, swine's flesh, said the wench.
What, my sweet old pigsnie be content, for if you live till next year, you will be a
foul sow. Walk knave, walk, said she, for if you live till next year, you will be a
fool."

Another of Dougal Graham's productions was "The History of Buchaven in Fifeshire,
Containing the witty and entertaining exploits of Wise Willie, and Witty Eppy, the Ale
Wife," the title always being modified by various publishers, a common occurrence with
chapbook titles, and contents. Wise Willie and Witty Eppy lived in a little house in
the little sea coast town of Buckyharbour. There, they decided controversies and explained their wonders.

Figure 42

Title page illustration from
"The Merry Tales of the Wise Men of Gotham."

"It happened on a day that two of their wives near the town, found a horse shoe,
and brought it home and sent for Willie to see what it was; Willie comes and looks at
it; Indeed, co' Willie, its a thing and holes in it. I kent, co' they, he wad get a
name till't. A' ho'! co' Willie, whar did ye find it? Aneath my Lord's ain house,
Willie. Adeed, said Willie, it's the auld moon. I ken by the holes in't, for nailing
it to the left; but I winder if she fell in Fyfe, for the last time I saw her, she was
hinging on her back aboon Edinburgh. A-hech, co' Willie, we'll set her upon the highest
house in the town, and we'll hae moonlight o' our ain a' the days o' the year. The
whole town ran to see the moon! Honest tout, said Witty Eppy, ye're but a' fools to-
gither; its but ane o' the things it my Lord's mare wears upon her lufe."

The chapbook from which the above extract was taken has been studied for the
richness of its folklore.

Various stories drawn from different sources, with Buchanan as their hero, were
written by Dougal Graham and published as "The Witty and Entertaining Exploits of George
Buchanan, who was commonly called, The Kings Fool." This chapbook was printed in Falkirk, Edinburgh, Glasgow, Aberdeen, Newcastle and other places. It is a pity that some
of Graham's as well as other chapbooks cannot be here reproduced in full, but it is
hoped that the extracts will give one an idea of the types of their contents.

Much more could be written of the various humorous chapbooks and even their
titles alone would occupy many pages. I know that I have failed to mention other popular and entertaining ones, but this is due to limitations of space and not to any limit
of inclinations.

Chapter 18

OF HUMOROUS METRICAL TALES FOUND IN CHAPBOOKS

The humorous metrical tale chapbooks could have been included with those of the previous chapter, depending upon one's personal opinion. However, it seems best to treat them separately. Although not a large group in comparison with some of the others, it contains a representative number of pieces. The history of Tom Thumb belongs here, also the diverting history of John Gilpin, the wife of Bath, Watty and Meg, the monk and the miller's wife, Jack Horner, Jack and Jill, Jack Sprat, the churlish husband, the comical history of the collier's wedding, and others that are more or less familiar.

"The History of Tom Thumb" has long been popular, not only in chapbooks, but in other printed versions also. Reginald Scott, in his "Discovery of Witchcraft," printed in 1584, speaking "Of vaine apparitions, how people have been brought to feare bugges," mentions "Tom thombe" along with the giants, imps, fairies, satyrs, witches, goblins, etc., with which "in our childhood our mothers maids have so terrified us." And Thomas Nashe in "Pierce Penilesse His Supplication to the Diuell" (1592) grumbles that "eury grosse braind Idiot is suffered to come into print, who if hee set foorth a Pamphlet of the praise of Pudding-pricks, or write a Treatise of Tom Thumme, or the exploits of Vntruss; it is bought vp thicke and threefold, when better things lie dead."

In 1621 the tale appeared, in prose, in Richard Johnson's "The History of Tom Thumbe the Little, for his small stature surnamed King Arthur's Dwarfe: Whose Life and aduentures containe many strange and wonderfull accidents, published for the delight of merry Time-spenders." Tom Thumb also appears in Drayton's "Nymphidia" (1627) and it would be possible to mention other notable instances where Tom Thumb has been utilized to advantage, such as Fielding's burlesque, "Tom Thumb A Tragedy" (1730) and Kane O'Hara's "Tom Thumb; A Burletta, Altered from Henry Fielding" (1830).

The earliest Tom Thumb in Europe appears to be the Thaumlin or Little Thumb of the Northmen, a dwarf of Scandinavian descent. The popular Danish history of Svend Tomling treats of "a man no bigger than a thumb, who would be married to a woman three ells and three quarters long." Then there is the "Daumerling," a little Thumb of the Germans, who is swallowed by a dun cow. It is said that the German and Danish "Thumb" stories contain much that is found in the northern versions. In India Tom Thumb has his counterpart in the Khodra Khan of the Mohammedans. In the Hindoo story. Vamuna is so tiny that he thinks the water-filled impression of a cow's hoof in the earth is a lake and he begs King Mahabali for a piece of ground over which he may walk in three strides.

Tom Thumb, a comic story, belongs to one of the groups or divisions of the so-called Swallow cycle. The hero is swallowed by a cow, a giant, a fish, a miller and a salmon, and escapes from all in safety. According to Macculloch, many swallow myths gradually change into stories which attempt to account for various natural events. The curiosity of man makes him invent stories explaining such events. Or an inventive story-teller might build upon an old myth. Many folk-tales of various countries have been changed and modified during the passage of centuries, yet they retain some common characteristics and enough of their antiquity to identify them as the remains of beliefs, customs and ideas of a forgotten age.

In this account, however, we shall not go back beyond the 1630 edition of Tom Thumb, which was bequeathed to the Bodleian Library by the author of the "Anatomy of Melancholy." This small black letter edition bears the title "Tom Thumbe, his life and

death: wherein is declared many maruailous acts of manhood, full of wonder, and strange
merriments. Which little knight lived in King Arthur's time, and famous in the court
of Great Brittaine. London, printed for John Wright. 1630." The ballad, consisting of
135 lines, opens as follows:

> In Arthurs court Tom Thumbe did liue,
>   A man of mickle might,
> The best of all the table round,
>   And eke a doughty knight:
>
> His stature but an inch in height,
>   Or quarter of a span;
> Then thinke you not this little knight,
>   Was prou'd a valiant man?
>
> His father was a plow-man plaine,
>   His mother milkt the cow,
> But yet the way to get a sonne
>   "This" couple knew not how,
>
> Until such time this good old man
>   To learned Merlin goes,
> And there to him his deepe desires
>   In secret manner showes,
>
> How in his heart he wisht to have
>   A childe in time to come,
> To be his heire, though it might be
>   No bigger than his Thumbe.

Figure 43

Brave Tom Thumb who beat all comers.

Figure 44

Tom Thumb about to fall into the pudding bowl.

Merlin told the plowman that his wish would come true and Tom was eventually
"begot and borne in halfe an houre" and in four minutes he grew as tall as the plowman's thumb. Of course he was under the protection of the fairies, and at his

christening, which was attended by the "Fayry-Queene" with her "traine of Goblins grim," he was named Tom Thumb. Little is told of his early childhood. The fairy queen clothed him in garments which lasted many years, a hat made of an oak leaf, a shirt of a spider's web, his hose and doublet of thistle down, his garters, two little hairs pulled from "his mothers eye" and his boots and shoes from a mouse's skin. Thus attired he sallies forth to play with the neighboring children, losing his "cherry stones," stealing a fresh supply from his playmates, indulging in such tricks as hanging "Black pots, and glasses upon a bright sunnebeame," and laughing at the whippings which the other boys received when their attempts to do the same ended in broken crockery. Because of the turmoil which Tom created when he went out to play, his mother kept him at home, and from then on his adventures commenced in earnest.

> He sate vpon the pudding-boule,
>   The candle for to hold;
> Of which there is vnto this day
>   A pretty pastime told:
>
> For Tom fell in, and could not be
>   For euer after found,
> For in the blood and batter he
>   Was strangely lost and drownd.

Although his mother searched long, it was in vain, and unknowingly she thrust her son into the pudding and the pudding into the kettle. But the pudding bounced around so violently that she thought the devil was inside and very charitably she bestowed it upon a passing tinker. Tom's voice issuing from the pudding scared the tinker so that he threw it down and ran. Tom then emerged adn returned home, but only to get into fresh trouble. When Tom's mother went to milk her cows, she tied him fast to a thistle so that the blustery wind would not blow him away, but alas, a cow came by and ate the thistle, Tom and all, and Tom traveled the entire length of the cow's alimentary canal. His next escapade happened while he was helping his father plow. He fell into the furrow, and was carried away, just like a grain of corn, by a raven and

> Unto a giants castle top,
>   In which he let him fall,
> Where soone the giant swallowed vp
>   His body, cloathes and all.
>
> But in his belly did Tom Thumbe
>   So great a rumbling make,
> That neither day nor night he could
>   The smallest quiet take,
>
> Until the gyant had him spewed
>   Three miles into the sea,
> Whereas a fish soone tooke him vp
>   And bore him thence away.

The fish was caught and sent to King Arthur. Tom was discovered and enjoyed high favor at court. He danced a "galliard braue vpon his queenes left hand," went on hunting trips with the king, paid a visit to his parents, who feasted him three days on a hazel nut, and returned to King Arthur's court where he engaged in tournaments, vanquishing all his opponents to the great amazement of the knights, but as a result of such strenucus exertions finally becoming sick, and dying, in spite of the skill and cunning of King Arthur's physician.

> And so with peace and quietnesse
>   He left this earth below;
> And vp into the Fayry Land
>   His ghost did fading goe.

He received by the Fairy Queen "with musicke and sweet melody" and King Arthur, after mourning with his knights for forty days, built a tomb of marble gray," "in remembrance of his name."

Figure 45.

Tom Thumb dancing a galliard
on the Queen's left hand.

Thus ends what appears to be the original tale of Tom Thumb, but the story was amplified by the addition of a second and third part, both detailing fresh adventures but lacking the charm and quaintness of the original version. Hazlitt has stated that the author of these later parts was "not trammelled by rhythm, grammar or geography." The second part commences with Tom's return from fairyland and his fall "into a pan of firmity," in good King Edgar's court, causing the cook to drop the pan and mess things up generally. Tom was dragged over to the king's table, where

> With clubs and staves, forks and prongs,
>   He guarded was, unpitied,
> To answer for the mighty Wrongs,
>   Which he had there committed.

Just as they began to vote on what form his death should take, Tom escaped from such an unfriendly atmosphere by jumping down a miller's throat and in addition to whistling, singing and dancing,

> Tom often pinch'd him by the tripes,
>   And made the Miller roar,
> Alas! alas! ten thousand stripes
>   Could not have vex'd him more.

After calling in the doctor and twenty learned men and after confessing to various thefts, the miller jumped in a river "and turn'd Tom Thumb into the tide," where he was swallowed by a salmon which was caught and finally purchased by the king's steward. Tom was brought before the king, impaled on a fork, but the affairs of state were not to be interrupted then by such a slender cause and so the cook was instructed to keep Tom a prisoner, which he did by binding him hand and foot and placing him in a mouse trap. After an interval of a week, Tom was taken before the king, but he made such a good plea that he was pardoned and taken into favor.

His troubles, however, were not at an end. While riding on a mouse, ahunting with the king, a farmer's cat captured both and ran to the top of a tree. After a sad and bloody fight during which the cat scratched and Tom ran his sword through her, the cat dropped him. From this encounter he did not recover. His injuries were too severe. And so the fairy queen sent "a mighty swarm of pretty Fairy Sprites" for him.

> They put him in a winding sheet,
>   More white than Lillies fair,
> These Fairies all with music sweet
>   Did mount the lofty air.

But "death's fatal arrows prov'd in vain," because "he was hurried back again down from Fairy Land," and a third part of the tale deals with "his Marvellous Acts of Manhood, performed after his second return from Fairy Land." His first adventure, however, after reaching the earth was so undignified and so devoid of romanticism that only in a "limited and unexpurgated" edition would it be proper to mention it. In due course Tom finally appeared before King Thunston's court where he underwent another trial, coming through, as usual, with honors and ingratiating himself with the king. In fact the king thought so highly of Tom that he bought him a coach drawn by six mice and he lived in splendid ease. But horrors! the microscopic wretch attempted to ravish the queen and,

> The Queen, with rage and fury fir'd,
>   To see herself abus'd,
> That of the King she then desir'd,
>   Tom Thumb might be accus'd.
>
> That nothing would her wrath appease,
>   To free her from all strife,
> Or set her mind at perfect ease,
>   Until she had his life.

Tom escaped this time on a butterfly which after giving him an uncomfortable ride, unluckily flew back to the court where Tom was discovered and captured. He was brought to trial, a very sick man, and

> So the King his sentence he declar'd.
>   How hanged he should be,
> And that a Gibbet should be rear'd,
>   And none should set him free.

Tom was imprisoned in a mousetrap, but a cat, mistaking him for a mouse, broke his prison and in endeavoring to escape he fell into a spider's web.

> The spider, watching for his Prey,
>   Tom took to be a fly,
> And seized him without delay,
>   Regarding not his cry.
>
> The blood out of his body drains,
>   He yielded up his breath;
> Thus he was freed from all Pains
>   By his unlook'd for death.
>
> Thus you have heard his actions all,
>   Likewise his actions great,
> His Rise, his Progress, and his fall,
>   Thus ushered in by fate.
>
> Although he's dead, his Memory lives,
>   Recorded ever sure;
> His very name some pleasure gives,
>   And ever will endure.

This in brief is the story of Tom Thumb as told in three parts. During the reigns of James I, Charles I and Charles II, Tom Thumb enjoyed continued popularity, and he was frequently mentioned by contemporary authors. Ritson in 1791, when he reprinted the 1630 version of Tom Thumb in his "Pieces of Ancient Popular Poetry" (London), said that every city, town, village, shop, stall, man, woman and child in the kingdom" was familiar with it. John Newbery published editions in 1768, 1786 and 1789. Various versions circulated as chapbooks down to the beginning of the nineteenth century and even later.

Ever since the story has been current, Tom's thrilling adventures have been told and retold, with modifications by each generation, and many variations occur in the numerous editions within a generation. Although the coarseness of the seventeenth century would not be permitted to circulate in the nurseries of today, it should be remembered that in the seventeenth century Tom Thumb was as popular with adults as with children, and no doubt some of the allusions in the early accounts were not intended particularly for childish understanding.

Some of the liberties taken with the text appear to be quite unnecessary. In present-day versions, no one will object to the deletion of expressions which are now highly unconventional and which are objectionable to those of squeamish sensibilities-- at least not so long as the early versions are obtainable. However, nearly every one who has arranged the tale for publication has made changes, probably under the delusion that the original was being improved upon. And so in some present-day accounts we are told that Merlin, because the plowman's wife refused him admittance to her home, when he was cold, revenged himself by seeing to it that her baby boy grew no bigger than her thumb. The thistle which the cow ate in 1630 has now become a buttercup. Tom's hat is made, not of an oak leaf but of a rose leaf. And under no circumstances is Tom now allowed to get beyond the cow's mouth. His mother either saves him in time or the cow sneezes him to safety or the cow, hearing strange noises in her throat, simply opens her mouth without further ado and Tom falls out.

The real reason for the queen's displeasure with Tom is never even hinted at. That of course would be unthinkable, and so the Queen is made to appear jealous because Tom gets a coach and six mice, or no reason is given at all. Kisses have been injected into modern versions also. Tom's mother kisses him after he escapes from the pudding a and before she puts him to bed. Such an act of endearment seems strangely out of place in Tom Thumb's life. He is not at all kissable, and his adventures are not the sort that admit expressions of affection. But when "adapters" and "arrangers" go so far as to have Tom place carpet tacks in the path of the cat--then something should be done about it.

Many years ago, Dr. Wagstaffe concluded that although Tom Thumb was looked upon merely as entertainment for children, it was "perhaps a performance not unworthy the perusal of the judicious." Dr. Wagstaffe believed that the design of the tale to recommend virtue and to demonstrate that "however any one may labour under the disadvantages of stature and deformity, or the meanness of parentage, yet if his mind and actions are above the ordinary level, those very disadvantages that seem to depress him add a lustre to his character." Even now some of our "adapters" show a trace of Hannah More-ism at the ends of their adaptations, but for the most part Tom Thumb has been fortunate in escaping the clutches of the moralists.

According to tradition, Tom Thumb died at Lincoln, which was one of the five Danish towns of England, and according to the same tradition his tombstone was a little blue flagstone, in the cathedral, which has long since disappeared. Although the authenticity of this remains uncertain, there can be no doubt about Tom Thumb himself being very much alive today, which is my excuse for bringing him up, as Thomas Nashe has said, "thicke and threefold, when better things lie dead."

"The Diverting History of John Gilpin," written by William Cowper in 1782, is a humorous ballad that was once sung in the streets and that circulated in newspapers, magazines, chapbooks and even yet appears in illustrated editions of its own. The ballad relates how the well-to-do linendraper John Gilpin, upon the advice of his wife, agreed to celebrate their marriage of twenty years by a family dinner at the Bell at Edmonton. Mrs. Gilpin, her sister and four children went in the chaise and Mr. Gilpin was to follow on horseback. The horse, however, ran away with Mr. Gilpin, through Edmonton, never stopping until it reached Ware. And although Gilpin headed him back, he couldn't stop him until London was reached. During the ride John Gilpin lost his hat, his wig, his coat, two bottles of wine, and his dignity. Children screamed, dogs barked and great excitement was caused by his wild ride.

In common with other popular writings, Cowper's ballad did not escape additions in the shape of second and third parts, written by persons who expected to benefit from the popularity of the original. Various and numerous editions of John Gilpin have been published, some finely illustrated, but not many of them can be classified as chapbooks. The ballad was written when the chapbook age was waning. However, John Gilpin chapbooks were published in London, Dublin, Birmingham, Newcastle, Hull, Dartford, and other places. Catnach, of course, published an edition illustrated with woodcuts.

The "Courtier and the Jovial Tinker" is a collection of tales,--"1. How finding a drunken tinker asleep, he had him carried in that posture to his house; laid him on a bed in a stately room, with rich cloaths by him, feasted and entertained him with musick, and making him drunk, conveyed him back again.--2. How he bought all the butter of a woman going to market, and the frolics he played with her for being over covetous, causing the saying, when a woman scratches her, butter will be cheap.--3. By what a comical method he relieved the poor widow of Mortlake against the Parson of the Parish, who had stopped up her water-gap.--4. How he served the tinker coming again to his house, because he complained he could get no drink.--5. A comical trick he made the tinker serve an old farmer, who used to ride sleeping, making him think that his horse was a devil.-- 6. How the tinker complained to him of a butcher's dog that often assaulted him; how he put on the tinker's habit, fought with and killed the dog, and the comical examination before a Justice."

All you that jovial tinkers are,
    Come listen unto me;
I dream'd a dream that was so rare,
    That none to it can e'er compare,
        No tinker such did see.

I thought I was a king indeed,
    Attired gay and fine:
In a stately palace I did tread,
Was to a princely banquet led,
        And had good cheer of wine.

But soon I found me in a ditch,
    That did no comfort lend:
This shows a tinker, tho' he itch
To be a prince or to grow rich,
        Must still old kettles mend.

Figure 46

Some events in "The Pleasant History of Jack Horner."

"The Pleasant History of Jack Horner, containing his witty Tricks and pleasant Pranks which he play'd from his youth to his riper years, right pleasant and delightful for winter and summer's recreation" was another favorite, especially with the publishers of children's chapbooks. In the following lines from an edition published about 1760 in Newcastle, one may see what appears to be the origin of the popular nursery rhyme.

> Jack Horner was a pretty lad,
>   Near London he did dwell;
> His father's heart he made full glad,
>   His mother lov'd him well.
> A pretty boy of curious wit,
>   All people spoke his praise,
> And in the corner he would sit
>   In Christmas holy-days:
>
> When friends they did together meet,
>   To pass away the time,
> Why, little Jack, he sure would eat
>   His Christmas-pye in rhime,
> And said, Jack Horner, in the corner,
>   Eats good Christmas pye,
> And with his thumb pulls out the plumb,
>   And said, Good boy am I.

A popular poem at one time was "The New Wife of Beath, much better reformed, enlarged, and corrected, than it was formerly in the old uncorrect copy. With the addition of many other things." This is a Glasgow title of the year 1700, in black-letter. The poem may be traced back to a thirteenth century fable. An edition published in Glasgow about 1850, is entitled "The Wife of Beith; being An Allegorical Dialogue, containing nothing but what is in scripture." The poem is concerned with the difficulty the Wife of Beith had in getting into heaven.

> In Beith once dwelt a worthy wife,
> Of whom brave Chaucer mention makes
> She lived a licentious life,
> And namely in venereal acts
> But death did come for all her cracks;
> When years were spent and days outdriven,
> Then suddenly she sickness takes,
> Deceased forthwith, and went to heaven.

Figure 47

Jack getting his ears cuffed,
From "The Friar and the Boy."

"The Comical story of Thrummy Cap, and the ghaist" by John Burness appeared frequently in chapbooks, sometimes accompanied by other pieces such as "Margaret and the Minister," "William and his little dog," and "Soda water." Thrummy Cap and a friend encounter, while staying at an inn over night, the ghost of a man who could not rest on account of his theft of some deeds to an estate. Eventually everything is straightened out.

Other titles belonging to this group of humorous metrical tales are "The notted (sic) History of Mother Grim, commonly called Goody Grim's witty Tales, very curious for a winter evening," "Love in a barn; or, Right country courtship, shewing how a London lord was tricked by a farmer's daughter, "The friar and boy; or, The young piper's pleasant pastime. Containing his witty pranks, in relation to his step-mother, whom he fitted for her unkind treatment," "The London butcher; or the miser outwitted," "The crafty chambermaid; or Beauty and virtue rewarded," and "Raising the wind; or, Habbie-Sympson & his wife baith dead. As originally written and spoken by John Andrews in the exchange rooms, Moss street. Together with The lyfe and deithe of Habbie Simpson, the

Figure 48

An old man begging food from Jack.
From "The Friar and Boy."

famous pyper of Kilbarchan, written by Robert Sempill, of Belltreis, between the years 1630 and 1640." This last title was published by G. Caldwell at Paisley and is, according to Fraser, one of the chapbooks which supplies the choicest specimens of national humor, customs, and manners of Scotland.

Chapter 19

OF CHAPBOOKS ON DREAMS, FORTUNE TELLING AND LEGERDEMAIN

If you wanted to see your future husband or wife, or to know the significance of moles, or if you wanted to practice the art of hocus-pocus, or have your dreams interpreted, or to know how to make sport with an egg, or how to eat fire, or to be able to perform the newest tricks with cards and dice, you had only to consult several of such chapbooks upon these subjects. Although not plentiful from the standpoint of titles, it is quite likely that numerous copies of some titles were printed and sold.

"The Conjurer's Magazine of secrets in Legerdemain & Slight of Hand; containing every experiment that is either Curious, Pleasing, Entertaining or Surprizing, as performed By The Most Celebrated Professors: forming A rich Store of never-ceasing Amusement. Including All the New Discoveries. By W. Ramsay, Author of Astrologia Redivivus, &c., &c.," is a twenty-four-page chapbook printed in London by Hodgson & Co. For the small sum of sixpence, one could find out from this book of wonders how to do a droll trick with a fowl, how to make a calf's head bellow, as if alive, when dressed or served up, how to make sport with an egg and also with a sheep's bladder, how to nail a card to the wall by a pistol shot, how to blow sixpence out of another man's hand, how to make a person tumble and toss all night, and not be able to sleep, how to make an artificial spider, that moves by electricity, how to make sport with a cat, and how to cut off a man's head, and to put the head into a platter a yard from his body, as well as how to do other tricks.

To make sport with a cat, one is told to tie a little bell on the end of its tail. Or if you prefer you may fasten walnut shells with a little warm wax or pitch to tabby's feet. This is delightful, and at night on the stairs, she will sound like a ghost going up and down. To make a person tumble and toss all night, the reader is advised to get some roach alum, pound it very small, and sprinkle between the sheets. If roach alum is not available, then horse hair cut up fine will do. "To cause the beer you drink to seem to be wrung out of the handle of a knife," requires a sponge previously soaked in beer, placed privately behind your right ear. Then have your audience before you. Stick a knife in the table with the handle upwards. Tell the company to see for themselves that the table and knife are dry, "then stretch your empty hand toward your ear, darting the point, saying 'Now somebody cross my arm'; and speaking some powerful words, as 'Jubio bisco'; then have you a fair opportunity to take the sponge into your hand from behind your ear, and stretching forth your hand, squeeze it gently, and after a little harder, which makes it run faster." Then sprinkle a little in the eyes of the company while you convey away the sponge.

There was "The Egptian Fortune-Teller, in two parts; stating proper questions for men in the first part, and for the women in the second part," in both verse and prose. In considering love and marriage, "If a hare cross you in the morning, it is a sign of some loss, or sickness; but if it pass by on your right hand, it is a token of marriage and good fortune. If you dream that a red-breast brings you a green bough in its mouth, it betokens marriage and many children."

In "Love's True Oracle, or a new and curious fortune-book for men, maids, wifes, and widows, plainly and truly resolving, after a new and ingenious method, whether life be long or short," one finds the following remedy for averting witchcraft, and for preventing a thief from breaking into the house. "Pimpernal, governed by the sun, being gathered in the latter end of July half an hour after two in the afternoon, or something more: take this herb, and sew it up in a yellow silk rag, stiched with yellow silk, and lay it under the threshold, hindereth the witch from coming in, and dissolveth witchcraft;

or take a quill of quicksilver, and stop it with yellow wax very well, and lay it under the party bewitched, and the inchantment will cease."

To know whether the party you love is real, the advice in "The High German Fortune-teller," is to "steep rose-leaves in vinegar. Then dry 'em to powder. Add a little of the powder of nightshade to 'em, and give about a dram of it to the party in wine or other liquor; and if he, or she smiles, or the amorous gestures don't make it all apparent, or some words fall more than usual, then be confident there's nothing in it." In this chapbook one may make love powders in several ways, one being as follows. "Take bay-berries, and gum of ivy, fern-root, and the claws of a crab; dry 'em to powder; and sift them thro' a fine sieve, and if you want to know anyone's affection, put a dram of it into a glass of wine, or other liquor, and it will work strange effects, without injuring the health of the party."

The following "love-observations on first hearing the cuckoo," are amusing and appear in "Aristotle's Legacy; or his Golden Cabinet of Secrets opened, in five treatises." "When you walk abroad in the spring, as soon as you hear the cuckoo, sit down on a bank, or any convenient place, and pull the stocking from off your right leg, and whilst you are doing it, say:

> May this to me
> Now lucky be.

"Then looking between your great toes, and you'll perceive a hair, which will easily come off; take it, and look well on it, and you will perceive it to be the colour (of) the party's hair you desire. Wrap it up in a piece of paper, and keep it ten days carefully. If then it has not changed colour, then the party loved will be constant, and you will obtain your desire; but if it do, you are flattered, and will be deceived." This chapbook covers fortune telling by palmestry, physiognomy and metocopy, and also includes a treatise on moles, observation on St. Valentine's day, etc., etc., in its twenty-four pages, and is also illustrated by forty-eight cuts.

Figure 49

Title page illustration from
"The History of Mother Bunch."

"Mother Bunch's Golden Fortune-Teller" was a popular one and was concerned with affairs of the heart, as usual, and with the art of fortune telling by coffee grounds, tea grounds, important signs, secret writing, etc., and with the making of "dumb cake." According to Mother Bunch, "They who have their nails broad, are of gentle disposition, bashful, and afraid of speaking before their superiors, or indeed to any without hesitation and a downcast eye. If around the nails there is usually an excoriation, or sprouting of the skin, the person is luxurious, fearful, and an epicure, loving enjoyment, provided it is to be obtained without danger. When there are certain white marks at the end, it testifies that the person is improvident, soon ruining their fortune through negligence. When the end is black, the man loves agriculture. Round nails declare a hasty person. When the nails are long, the person is good natured, but placing confidence in no man, being from his youth conversant in deceit, yet not practising it, from the goodness of his nature and a love of virtue."

"Partridge and Flamstead's New and well experienced Fortune Book" was another popular one dealing with fortune telling by cards, the significance of moles, the interpretation of dreams, and including a dialogue between "The Whimsical Lady and Her Lover." The text relative to telling fortunes by cards is in verse. Opposite the ace of diamonds, it is stated

> Since this Ace it seems your lot
> You'll wed one that's fierce and hot,
> But if Women-kind draws it,
> She'll have one with wealth and wit.

And for the ace of spades, it is said

> Thou who get'st the Ace of Spades,
> Shall be flouted by the maids
> But should it be a damsel's lot,
> Love and honor go to pot.

Figure 50

A Catnach dream book.

Many of the chapbooks on fortune telling are more or less similar in their contents--although changes in text and arrangement may be noted. And of course, some were illustrated and a few even had colored frontispieces. Others were devoid of illustrations. As to moles, the significance of them was about the same in all chapbooks.

"A mole on the middle of the forehead denotes riches and advancement by the favour of friends.

"A mole between the eyes, inclining towards the nose denotes the person to grow rich by marriage.

"A mole on the left lip signifies the party shall be rich by the death of relatives.

"A mole on the back demonstrates much labour and sorrow.

"A mole on the right knee promises success in love and several marriages."

And so on, until most of the human anatomical parts have been covered--by moles.

J. Catnach, of Monmouth Court, Seven Dials, London, published the "Dreamer's Oracle," with a large colored illustration on the title page, and with a few black and white illustrations in the text. The things dreamed of are arranged alphabetically.

"Angels. To dream you see angels, is a sure sign that some one is near you--if a woman with child dreams of them, she will have a good time, perhaps twins.

"Bat. To dream of a bat is very inauspicious. Yet the bat is good indeed to women with child.

"Capon. To dream that a capon crows, signifies sadness and trouble.

"Death. Denotes happiness and long life; that you will either be speedily married yourself, or else assist at a wedding. To dream you see another person dead, denotes ill usage from friends.

"Mad. To dream you are mad is very good--it promises long life, riches, happy marriage, success in trade, dutiful children--and, if a farmer, good crops.

"Thunder. Dreaming of thunder signifies affliction to the rich; but to the poor repose.

"Winds. To dream of high winds, storms and showers of rain, shows you will be crossed in love."

Figure 51

Fortune telling by cards.
From "The Circle of Fate."

Figure 52

From the "Circle of Fate,"
a fortune-telling chapbook published
by J. Catnach.

Catnach and his successors issued other similar chapbooks, carrying such titles as "The Circle of Fate; or, True Norwood Gipsey," "The Universal Fortune-Teller," etc. In addition to what has been noted as common to all such chapbooks, advice on charms, how to choose a husband by the hair, and spells, were frequently included. "A Curious Spell. If a maid wishes to see her lover, let her take the following method. Prick the third or wedding finger of your left hand, with a sharp needle (beware of a pin) and with the blood, write your own and lover's name on a piece of clean writing paper, in as small a compass as you can, and encircle it with three round rings of the same crimson stream, fold it up, and exactly at the ninth hour of the evening bury it with your own hand in the earth, and tell no one. Your lover will hasten to you as possible, and he will not be able to rest until he sees you, and if you have quarrelled, to make it up. A young man may also try this charm, only instead of the wedding finger, let him pierce his left thumb."

Sometimes the "evil and perilous days in every month of the year" were noted. For example, "In January are eight days, that is the 1st, 2nd, 4th, 5th, 10th, 15th, 17th, and 19th." No reasons are given and January has more than any other month. There were also "Observations on Birth, Commonly called Nativity" and under the name of every month, good and bad signs were interpreted. As to physiognomy, "A great nose shows a good man; a little nose, a deceitful person. A sharp nose denotes an angry person and a scold; thick and low, a person of bad manners; the nose stretching to the mouth denotes honesty, strength, and aptness to learning. Thin lips with a little mouth, shows an effeminate person; slender, thin, and fine lips betoken eloquence. Fleshy and great lips a fool. And those whose front teeth project are generally contumelious, slanderous, and unfaithful; also much addicted to the love of strange women."

OLD HARRY,
THE RAREE-SHOW-MAN.

LONDON:
PUBLISHED BY J. BYSH
9 Crescent Place, Upper Grange Road Bermondsey.

Figure 53
Title page of
"Old Harry, The Raree-Show-Man."

Love Dreams Expounded in Verse

Dreams of rivers, ships, and horses,
Of snow or frost, or of dead corpses,
Are signs by which it might be read,
Your sweetheart's love is cold or dead.

If maidens dream of drawing drink
In cellars, they may walking think
That their sweethearts, without delay,
Will leave them soon and run away.

To dream of rivers or of water
Doth signify much weeping after;
If dreams of drowning fright the fair,
They of their virtue must take care.

Dreams of joy and pleasant jests,
Dancing, merriment and feasts;
Or any dreams of recreation,
Signify love's declaration.

Chapter 20

OF CHAPBOOKS ON DEMONOLOGY AND WITCHCRAFT

Although not exceptionally numerous from the standpoint of titles, chapbooks on wtichcraft must have been popular in view of the commonly accepted beliefs about demons and witches. Satan, Doctor Faustus, the Lancashire witches, wizards, diabolical practices, Friar Bacon, examinations, confessions, trials and executions, and the expulsion of devils all appear in the chapbook literature of witchcraft, in amounts ranging from as few as six to as many as ninety pages.

"The Witch of the Woodlands, or the Cobler's New Translation" deals with an old, merry, conceited cobbler of Kent who gets into the power of witches, who transform him into a fox, a horse, and a swan. In the end he meets a beggar, who leaves him a fortune. The chapbook takes up successively, his place of abode, his marriage to a "wench," his escape, his journey to London, his good fortune and his return home.

Figure 54

Title page illustration from
"The History of the Learned Friar Bacon."

In 1627 a black-letter edition appeared entitled, "The Famous History of Fryer Bacon, containing the wonderfull things that he did in his life; also the manner of his death, with the lives and deaths of the two conjurers, Bungye and Vandermast. Very pleasant and delightful to be read." This was printed in London by "G.P., for Francis Grove." Friar Bacon, the son of a wealthy farmer, was born in the west of England. He was taught by the village parson until he learned everything the parson knew. His father, however, did not approve of book learning so Friar ran away and concluded his studies at Oxford. The king, having heard of his skill, sent for him and after arriving at court, Friar Bacon waved his wand and such excellent music was heard that everyone was amazed. Another wave of the wand, the music increased in volume, five dancers appeared, another wave and they disappeared. Another wave and a table richly covered with delicacies came into being. Additional wand waving brought and took away in succession, the smell of rich perfumes and representatives of various nations, in costume, who performed their native dances. The king was so pleased that he presented Friar Bacon with a costly jewel.

Friar Bacon's servant, one Miles, made believe to refrain from eating on fast days, but he always had food hidden away for such times and one day his master caused the pudding which Miles had prepared, in anticipation of a fast day, to stick in his mouth so that he could neither get it in nor out. But his master finally released him from such a predicament. Then follows an account showing "How Frier Bacon formed a Scheme whereby he could have walled England about with Brass, by making a Brazen Head to speak," etc.

Figure 55

The devil dancing around a circle for Dr. Faustus.

Another popular title was "The History of The wicked Life and horrid Death of Dr. John Faustus Shewing How he sold himself to the devil, to have power for 24 years to do what he pleased. Also strange things done by him and Mephostophiles. With an account how the devil came for him at the end of 24 years, and tore him to pieces." This is from a Glasgow edition, "Printed for the Book-sellers," and the account is a shuddering travesty of Goethe's beautiful story. The quotation of the following chapter from the chapbook should be sufficient.

"How Faustus made seven women dance naked in the Market Place.

"Faustus walking in the market-place, saw seven women sitting all in a row, selling eggs, butter, &c. Of every one he bought something and departed: No sooner was he gone, but all the eggs and butter were gone out of their baskets and they knew not how: At last they were told, that Dr. Faustus had conjured their goods away; they thereupon ran speedily to the Doctor's house, and so demanded satisfaction for the ware: He resolving to make himself and the town's people merry by his conjuring Art, made them return to their baskets naked as ever they were born: and having danced a while in the market place every one's goods were conjured into their baskets again and they set at liberty."

"The History of the Lancashire Witches containing The manner of their becoming such: their Enchantments, Spells, Revels, merry Pranks, raising Tempests and Storms, riding on Winds, &c., &c. To which is added, the Description of a Spell. Likewise a brief Treatise on Witches in general;--with several other remarkable things of note. The like never before published," is a sixteen-page, penny chapbook that was published by J. Turner of Coventry as well as by others. And it is illustrated by a few wood-cuts. Lancashire was always noted for its witches and Mother Cuthbert who lived there in a little hovel, at the bottom of a hill, with her two lusty daughters, after several mysterious happenings, joined the society of witches. She indulges in many pranks after this and enchants the mayor of the town, who had sentenced her to be whipped in public. Her daughters also become witches and one of them, in the shape of a mare, is revenged upon her false sweetheart. Once Mother Cuthbert enchants several thieves and takes away their money. These witches, for the most part, did considerable muttering and turned themselves into animals in order to achieve their ends. Mother Cuthbert became so perfect in her art and in her ability to revenge herself upon any person she pleased that the neighbors were afraid of offending her and so the old hag received many presents of milk, cakes, and custards, which enabled her to live in peace and comfort. At the end of this chapbook the printer set the following lines:

> Now, courteous Reader, I must bid adieu,
> And if you think more's been said than true,
> And that your time it hath been misapply'd,
> A better subject take - lay this aside.

Figure 56

Dr. John Faustus making his pact with the devil.

Witchcraft chapbook titles are just as interesting and curious as those of other chapbook subjects, and just as long too. Some examples of these are quoted. "Satan's invisible world discovered, detailing.....strange pranks played by the devil, together with a particular account of several apparitions, witches, and invisible spirits, to which is added the marvellous history of Major Weir and his sister;" "The discovery of witches; an answer to severall queries, lately delivered to the judges of assize for the county of Norfolk. And now published by Matthew Hopkins, witch-finder. For the benefit of the whole kingdome;" this was printed in London in 1647; another printed in London in 1645 was, "The examination, confession, triall, and execution of Joane Williford, Joan Cariden, and Jane Hott, who were executed at Feversham in Kent for being witches, on Monday, the 29 of Sep. 1645. Being a true copy of their evill lives and wicked deeds, taken by the major of Feversham and jurors for the said inquest. With the examination and confession of Elizabeth Harris, not yet executed. All attested under the head of Robert Greenstreet, major of Feversham." And there were chapbooks for and against witchcraft, but the latter were few in number, as represented by the following:- "The belief in witchcraft vindicated; proving from Scripture there have been witches, and from reason that there may be such still. In answer to a late pamphlet intituled The impossibility of witchcraft, etc. London 1712;" "The impossibility of witchcraft; plainly proving from Scripture and reason that there never was a witch, and that it is both irrational and impious to believe there ever was. In which the depositions against Jane Wenham, lately try'd and condemn'd for a witch, at Hertford, are confuted and expos'd. London, 1712." Both authors used the Scriptures to prove their points.

Chapter 21

OF CHAPBOOKS CONTAINING PROPHECIES

All chapbook prophets were remarkable. The predictions always came true and their percentages of error were negligible, if they existed at all. Donald Cargill was a wonderful prophet and he has been commemorated in a chapbook. Margaret Nicholson, whose prophecies were written on the walls of Bedlam, was another. Then there were Robert Nixon and famous Mother Shipton, as well as Don Johannes Gantier and William Lilly "student in astrologie" and their strange lives and remarkable predictions are all preserved for us in penny histories, or sixpence histories with elegantly engraved frontispieces.

Many persons have heard of Mother Shipton and even though her prophecies have been forgotten, her name still survives. She was quite a favorite with chapbook printers. Born in Knaresborough, near the Dropping Well, it is said that her father was a necromancer. Her mother, Agatha, was extremely poor and of a melancholic disposition. One day while sitting on the bank of a river, she was accosted by the devil in the shape of a handsome young man. This infernal chap married her and conducted her on horseback, as swiftly as the wind, to a stately mansion where she was clothed in rich garments. "Having dined, they began dancing, in the midst of which Agatha's lustful devil took her into a private room, and there he enticed her to lust." After this it thundered in a prodigious manner and poor Agatha was stripped of her gaudy attire and found herself in a dismal wood, where, by some invisible hand she was put in a chariot drawn by two flaming dragons, and carried through the air, back to her former cottage. Eventually Agatha gave birth to a baby girl and the child was afterward called Mother Shipton. It is needless to state that Mother Shipton's birth was attended by thunder and lightning. The baby was not beautiful as are all babies. Its body was long, its bones big, its eyes, "sharp and full of crooks, turnings and red pimples, giving such a light that they needed not a candle to dress her by." As soon as she was born she fell "agrinning" and laughing and the tempest ceased immediately.

As she grew up Mother Shipton played pranks that do not look well in print and finally married Toby Shipton, a carpenter. She recovered stolen property for her neighbors by naming the thieves and finally acquired a wide reputation as a cunning woman. Some of her prophecies are quoted, as they were published in the chapbooks.

"Before the Ouse bridge and Trinity church meet, they shall build it by day, and it shall fall by night, until they get the uppermost stone of Trinity church, to be the first stone of Ouse bridge.

"This came to pass, for Trinity church in York was blown down by a tempest, and Ouse bridge broke down by a rapid flood; and what they repaired by day, fell by night, 'till at last they laid the highest stone of the church, as the foundation of the bridge."

"A time shall come, when a ship shall come sailing up the Thames, 'till it is opposite to London, and the master of the ship asks the Captain why he wept, since he had made so good a voyage? and he shall say, Ah! what a great city was this, none in the world comparable to it, but now scarce a house left in it.

"This were verified after the dreadful fire in London, in 1666, not one house being left upon the Thames side from the Tower to the Temple."

And there were other predictions too, that all came true. Mother Shipton died at fifty-nine years of age and on her tomb the following epitaph was written:

Here lies she who seldom ly'd,
Whose skill so often has been try'd:
Her prophecies shall still survive,
And ever keep her name alive.

Figure 57

Title page illustration
from an Aldermary Church Yard edition of
"The History of Mother Shipton."

Figure 58

Mother Shipton in action.

Much more could be written of Mother Shipton's prophecies and in some chapbooks
it was customary to leave the interpretation of some to the reader because they concerned future times. These were such as -

The Fiery Year as soon as 'oer,
Peace shall then be as before
Plenty everywhere is found.
And men with swords shall plow
the ground.

———

The time shall come, when seas of Blood,
Shall mingle with a greater Flood.

At Edinburgh, for one place, there was printed "The Life and Prophecies of Mr.
Alex. Peden, Late Minister of the Gospel at New Glenluce, Galloway. And his Remarkable
Letter." Mr. Peden never married because a young woman wrongfully accused him of being
the father of her child. For the most part Mr. Peden's predictions referred to what
would befall sinners unless they mended their ways and what he predicted always came to
pass. He was not at all picturesque like Mother Shipton and he didn't predict anything
spectacular, and so now no one remembers even his name.

Sir Thomas Learmant of Fife gave out his prophecies in rhyme and was called
Thomas the Rhymer. And so we have a chapbook called, "Prophecies of Thomas the Rhymer;
the ancient Scotch prophet, Containing the wonderful fulfilment of many of his Predictions; and those not yet accomplished. Collected, Examined, and now Promulgated By Mr.
Allen Boyd, F.S.A. Sub-Deputy Janitor's Clerk in the College of Hayti." This chapbook
was printed at Stirling by W. Macnie, in 1828 and filled out its twenty-four pages by
an account of the battle of Bannockburn, and the "Cottager's Saturday Night."

Thomas the Rhymer is the author of many mystical prophecies about all the kings
of Europe, and he even stooped to the prediction of storms, but such were among his
first. "The pride of Spain, and the deceitful conduct of the French, as also concerning the Dutch, is all foretold," as well as many Scottish battles. His prophecies in
verse start out as follows, and they are not all easy to understand.

Scotland be sad now and lament,
    For honours thou has lost
But yet rejoice in better times,
    Which will repay the cost.

Tho' unto thraldom you should be
    Brought by your enemies;
You shall have freedom from them all,
    And enjoy your liberties.

Another prophet was Robert Nixon of Cheshire and his remarks were popular with publishers and readers of chapbooks alike. Thomas Richardson of Derby brought out his prophecies in a twenty-four-page chapbook called "Nixon's Original Cheshire Prophecy in doggrel verse: Published From An Authentic Manuscript, Found among the Papers of a Cheshire Gentleman, lately deceased; Together with the Prophecy At Large, From Lady Cowper's Correct Copy, In the reign of Queen Anne: With Historical and Political Remarks, in which its fulfilments, in many instances are accomplished. And Some Particulars of His Life, By John Oldmixon, Esq. and others."

Figure 59

Mother Shipton.

Figure 60

Robert Nixon, "a short squab fellow"
as portrayed in an Aldermary Church Yard chapbook.

Robert Nixon, the son of a farmer, was christened in the year 1467 and from his infancy was noted for his stupidity. During his youthful years he made several minor predictions, "But what rendered Nixon the most noticed was, that at the time when the battle of Bosworth field was fought between King Richard the Third and King Henry the Seventh, he stopt his team on a sudden, and with his whip pointing from one land to the other, cried, 'Now Richard! Now Harry!' several times; till at last he said, 'Now Harry, get over that ditch, and you gain the day.' This came to the ears of King Henry, who sent for him and no sooner had Nixon arrived at the court, than the king, wishing to test his ability, hid a diamond ring and asked Nixon for help in finding it. Nixon replied, "He who hideth can find." On the way to court Nixon said that he was going to be starved there.

The king gave Nixon the run of the palace and the kitchen was his special dwelling place. While the king was at his huntin-seat, the palace servants so teased Nixon that the officer in charge of him locked him up in a closet and forgot to set him at liberty for three days, with the result that he found him dead, of hunger, as Nixon had predicted for himself. Nixon predicted various private and public happenings and a few quotations from his Cheshire prophecy will display his talents.

"When a raven shall build in a stone lion's mouth on the top of a church in Cheshire, then a King of England shall be driven out of his kingdom, and never return more.

"A pond shall run with blood three days, and the cross-stone pillar in the forest sink so low into the ground, that a crow from the top of it shall drink of the best blood in England.

"A boy shall be born with three thumbs, and shall hold three kings' horses, while England shall be three times won and lost in one day.

"A raven is known to have built in a stone lion's mouth in the steeple of the church of Over, in the forest of Delamere. Not long before the abdication of King James, the wall spoken of fell down, and fell upwards; and in removing the rubbish, were found the bones of a man of more than ordinary size. A pond at the same time ran with water that had a reddish tincture, and was never known to have done so before or since.

"In the parish of Budworth, a boy was born, about eighteen years ago, with three thumbs; the youth is still living there."

And so the chapbook continues, with other predictions that came true, proving that Nixon was just as great a prophet as Partridge.

Chapter 22

OF CHAPBOOKS ON CRIME AND CRIMINALS

These were quite numerous, and no doubt popular, as public taste in such matters seems always to be uniform. To this group belong Jack Sheppard and Richard Turpin. Regardless of the romantic esteem surrounding these characters they were none the less criminals. All phases of crime were set forth in the chapbooks, in prose and verse, histories of notorious highwaymen, pirates, murderers, robbers, and trials, sentences, executions, confessions, dying behavior, dreadful warnings and memoirs of infamous and notorious characters. All of which is also found in the newspapers of today. Apparently there has always existed in most persons a certain sympathy for law-breakers. Perhaps our respectability is only a crust, a very thin one at that. It is difficult to select titles of chapbooks on crime, that were extremely popular, if we except Jack Sheppard, Richard Turpin, and Claude Duval. No doubt many were published over and over. Like the headlines of today, the title page frequently gave the important features of the crime and whetted the appetite for details.

Pirates were always popular and so was "The History and Lives of all the most notorious Pirates and their Crews." This chapbook covered them "from Captain Avery, who first settled at Madagascar, to Captain John Gow, and James Williams, his lieutenant, &c., who were hanged at Execution Dock, June 11th, 1735, for piracy and murder, and afterwards hanged in chains between Blackwall and Deptford, and in this edition continued down to the year 1735."

In London, Ann Lemoine published in 1801 the "Lives of most remarkable female robbers. The German princess, a robber and imposter; Moll Cutpurse, a pickpocket and highwayman; Mary Read, Anne Bonny, pirates; Nan Hereford, a cheat and imposter," all in forty-eight pages, with an engraved frontispiece. The titles of the "trial" chapbooks were frequently unduly long and those on executions were not much shorter. One of these, printed in Sherborne, and reprinted in London, in 1754, with a woodcut frontispiece, runs as follows, - "The last dying words of the noted John Poulter, alias Baxter, who was apprehended for robbing Dr. Hancock, of Salisbury.....and was executed.....25th of February, 1754. Containing the many useful discoveries he has made; with some precautions to secure horses from being stolen and houses from being broke open; very convenient for all families. To which is added, The life and adventures of Dennis Neal, alias Turpin the second....."

Very often the crime title-page was used to convey warnings to wild and wicked persons. For example, - "The servant maid's tragedy; or A dreadful warning to all wild and thoughtless young women. Being a true.....account of Elizabeth Parker.....who was courted by one William Gilton.....when he took an opportunity to ruin her.....but she proving with child.....he decoyed her into the fields and there cut her throat....." and again, "The reprobate's reward; or, A looking glass for disobedient children, giving an.....account of a barbarous murder committed on the body of Mrs. Wood.....by her own son.....and of the murder being found out by the apparition of the ghost....."

"The History of James Allen, the celebrated Northumberland piper" was a popular chapbook, containing, as it did, his adventures, exploits, enlistments, escapes, and finally his death in Durham jail, likewise "The History of Eugene Aram," who was convicted of the murder of Daniel Clark, fourteen years after the crime was committed.

Then there was "The history of the merry life and exploits of Capt. James Hind, the great robber of England, together with the close of his life at Worcester, where he was hanged, drawn, and quartered for high treason against the commonwealth." There were various editions of this. Still another type of criminal is represented by "A warning to the fair sex; or, The matrimonial deceiver, being the history of the noted George Miller, who was married to upwards of thirty different women on purpose to plunder them ....."

There is little doubt about some of the murders reported in chapbooks having actually taken place, but the accounts in many instances have been greatly elaborated upon and embroidered by nameless authors. These murders, like many murders were committed by unimaginative persons, and consequently, there is little of finesse about them. Disreputable husbands murder their wives and children and hang their aged mothers from trees. Mary Jones knocks her victim down with a quart pot and sticks a knife in him for good measure. Sawney Beane and his family rob and murder for twenty-five years and their victims number a thousand. And blood flows freely.

In only eight pages, one may read, "The History of Sawney Beane and His Family Robbers and Murderers: Who took up their abode in a cave, near the sea-side, where they lived twenty-five years, without going once to visit any city, town, or village. Computation, they robbed and murdered about one thousand persons, whom they eat, but at last, were happily discovered by a pack of blood-hounds; when Sawney Beane, his wife, eight sons, six daughters, eight grand-sons, and fourteen grand-daughters, were all seiz'd and executed, in manner here-after specified."

Sawney Beane was born in East Lothian about eight or nine miles east of Edinburgh. He earned his living by digging ditches and ran away with a vicious woman, both living in a rock by the sea shore. They had many children and grand-children, all of whom lived in the same manner as their parents and for twenty-five years they all stayed at home, and supported themselves by robbery and murder. "By this bloody method, and their living so retiredly from the world, they continued a long time undiscovered; there being no body able to guess how the people were lost, who went by the place where they lived. As soon as they had robbed any one, they used to carry off their carcases to their den, where cutting them in quarters they would pickle the mangled limbs, and afterwards eat them, these being their only subsistence."

The inhabitants of the neighboring area became alarmed at the loss of so many of their neighbors and sent spies out who never returned. Several honest travelers and inn-keepers were unjustly executed because of the disappearance of some persons. And Sawney Beane and his family of cutthroats continued to rob and kill and dismember people, until one victim escaped alive and exposed their hiding place. Whereupon his majesty in person, with four-hundred men together with bloodhounds, tracked them down to their cave. It was a dismal sight "to see such a number of arms, legs, thighs, hands, and feet of men, women and children, hung up in rows like dry'd beef, and a great many lying in pickle." In addition there was a large quantity of money, watches, rings, swords, pistols, clothing and other things belonging to the victims.

Sawney Beane and his whole family of depraved wretches were jailed in Edinburgh and without any trial, were mutilated and burned to death. They died without the least sign of repentance.

As late as 1866, a curious, eight-page chapbook was issued at Paisley, entitled "An Account of the Executions in Scotland for the past 200 Years." This contains the names and crimes of various persons and the dates of their executions, arranged by towns. Housebreaking, robbery, murder, vitriol throwing, and forgery were all punished by death and the same fate attended those convicted of consulting with the devil and practising sorcery. In the latter cases, some were strangled and burned, and others were burned alive. The oath of the general executioner of Great Britain is given as follows:

"I swear to hang or behead, and to draw and quarter, or otherwise destroy all felons and enemies to the peace of our Lord the King, and of his subjects duly sentenced according to Law, and I will do the like unto father, mother, sister or brother, and all other kindred whatsoever, without favour or hindrence. So help me God."

The chapbook further states that, "Thereupon a black veil is thrown over him at his rising when he is conducted out of the court, and amid the groaning of the assembly, the tolling of the death-bell, and the horrifying words of the city judge grating in his ears, 'Get thee hence, wretch.'"

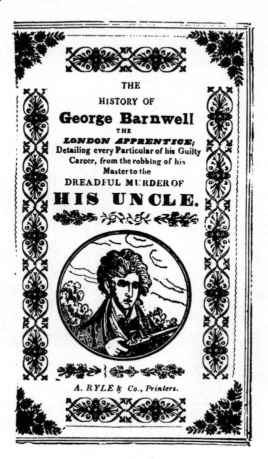

Figure 61

Cover page of
"The History of George Barnwell."

In "An Account of the Imprisonment and Execution of Poor Dennis An Irishman who was Hung for Robbery, and afterward restored to life by his Friends, and is now living in America!!! with an account Of a Highwayman whom he employed to Rob His Master," it is brought out that Dennis was a tall man and the gallows low, so that his feet touched the ground. After hanging a short time, he was cut down and given to his friends who carried him to a nearby cabin, where they applied restoratives, as this was the custom following all hangings. His feet were put in warm water, he was blooded with a rusty lancet in the hands of a countryman, he was rubbed with spirits, and some was poured down his throat. In this instance the methods succeeded. He opened his eyes and milk from a woman's breast was given to him, which in Ireland was considered a medicine of great efficacy. And so he recovered and went to America, otherwise this chapbook could not have been written.

According to the popular chapbooks on the "History of James Allan, the celebrated Northumberland Piper," our hero was born near Rothbury in 1734. He was a handsome youth with an acute and inventive mind, but he used his talents in promoting acts of low cunning and dissimulation. He also engaged in petty neighborhood thefts and learned

to excel on the pipes. During the course of his life he contracted an unfortunate marriage, drank deeply, joined the militia, deserted, was arrested, escaped, joined again,
deserted again, was captured and pardoned, married a gipsy princess, deserted her and
stole her savings, stole a silver tankard from a nobleman, was jailed, promised to marry
the jailor's daughter when she helped him to escape, failed to keep his promise, joined
another band of gipsies, deserted them, promised to enlist again but decamped after collecting his bounty in advance, was pursued and nearly captured several times, married
again, stayed sober, became intimate with a dissolute woman, grew tired of her, took up
with a gipsy girl, induced a captain's wife to elope with him and made off with her
clothes and valuables, was finally apprehended and committed to Durham jail, where he
finally died. All during his checkered career he played the pipes and charmed many persons with his music.

THE
PATHETIC HISTORY
OF
GEORGE BARNWELL.

Milwood persuading Barnwell to stay with her.

Figure 62.

Sarah Milwood exercising her wiles
upon George Barnwell.

Figure 63

Jack Sheppard illtreating Brown
and his wife, and taking the keys of St. Giles
watch-house.
From J. Catnach's "Life of Jack Sheppard."

John Gill was a different type of wretch and his exploits in the field of crime
were made the subject of a chapbook entitled "The Bloody Tragedy; Or a dreadful Warning
to disobedient children. Giving a dreaful account of John Gill, In the town of Woborn,
Bedfordshire, Who Lived a Wicked Life: How he murdered his Father and Mother by cutting
their Throats, from Ear to Ear; how he bound, ravished, and killed the servant maid, and
fired the house, burning the dead bodies to ashes, after he had stolen the plate and
money; how the ghost of the dead bodies appeared to him in Gaol, together with his dying
speech, &c. &c."

John Gill's father and mother were people of some substance in Bedfordshire, but
their only son was headstrong, wilful and spoiled. He broke the Sabbath, got drunk,
and finally a lewd woman persuaded him to rob his parents. One night he came home drunk
and requested that his parents give him money. They entreated him to go to bed and
promised him money in the morning. This apparently satisfied him, but he could not get
to sleep, and his evil spirit prompted him to arise and murder them. About midnight
this graceless son cut the throats of his mother and father and of the servant maid
also. After he set fire to the house, the ghosts of the murdered persons appeared before
him in frightful shape, pointing to their ghastly wounds, and summoning him to appear
before the tribunal of Almighty God to answer for their blood.

He eventually pleaded guilty and was sentenced to die. Just before his execution he delivered a speech, admitting his sins and asking for mercy from the Lord. After being cut down, he was hung in chains as a spectacle to all ungrateful wretcnes.

The following title page is so descriptive that no more need be said. "The Cruel Husband; or Devonshire Tragedy. Wherein is related the account of Mr. J. Barton, of Topsham. Who was put Apprentice to Mr. Long, merchant in Exeter, and afterwards married his master's maid-servant privately; but being threatened to be disinherited by his father for the same, was instigated by the Devil to murder her; which shocking act he committed. Also, A Remarkable Dream Of the Landlady where they lodged, discovering where the body of his wife was concealed; and his extraordinary penitence and execution." This eight-page chapbook was printed by J. Davenport, London, and sold for one penny.

Other popular titles included "The Life and Trial of Eugene Aram who was executed for the Murder of Daniel Clark, of Knaresborough," and "An Authentic History of the mysterious Murder of Maria Marten." In the case of Maria, her mother's dream led to the discovery of her body in a red barn. In fact, in the chapbook accounts dreams play an important part in either locating the body of the victim, or in torturing the murderer so that he confesses. In the case of the last chapbook murder that has been mentioned, there is even a plan of the red barn, showing the location of the corn room and calf-shed with respect to Maria's grave.

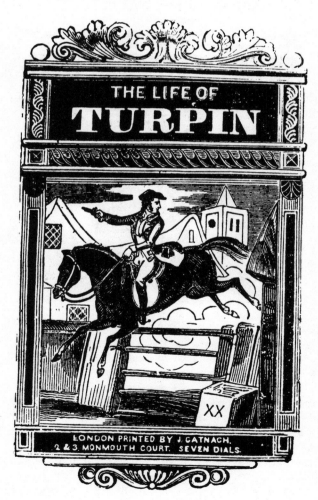

Figure 64
Cover page of Catnach's "Life of Turpin."

Another sordid murder was that committed by George Barnwell and detailed in "The History of George Barnwell the London Apprentice," who had a career of crime that started with the robbing of his master and ended with the murder of his uncle. Of course George was started on the downward path by an artful woman, one Sarah Milwood. In the language of the chapbook, "On a crimson damask sofa, placed under a brilliant mirror, illuminated with wax lights, the syren Milwood reclined. She did not rise as he entered, but holding out a most beautiful arm, encircled at the wrist with a brilliant bracelet, she motioned him to be seated. She touched the strings of a harp which lay near her, and the effect on Barnwell was instantaneous. Her embraces so infatuated him, as to destroy all his good resolutions, and his heart once more renounced his principles." And so he robbed his master of a hundred pounds for this despotic woman, who also suggested that he murder his uncle for more money. And he did, he shot him, and his uncle fell, weltering in gore. Barnwell made no speech at the place of execution, but it was observed that he wept bitterly after the cap was drawn over his eyes.

THE LIFE AND ADVENTURES
OF
RICHARD TURPIN,
A MOST
NOTORIOUS HIGHWAYMAN,
COMPRISING

Particular account of all his Robberies, His Ride to York, and his Trial and Execution for Horse-stealing, April 7th, 1739.

Figure 65

Richard Turpin putting the old woman on the fire
to make her tell where she had hidden her money.
From a Catnach chapbook.

Turning to a more picturesque thief and cutthroat we have Jack Sheppard, the famous house and prison breaker, who was at one time the hero of a pantomime and of a comic opera, and whose portrait was once painted by Sir James Thornhill. Jack Sheppard was a chapbook favorite. Catnach published one called "The Life and Adventures of Jack Sheppard, a most notorious housebreaker and footpad" and decorated it with illustrations. All London was aware of Jack's doings, of his various robberies, and of his wonderful escapes from different prisons. Twice he escaped from Newgate prison, and St. Giles' round-house could not hold him. Numerous robberies were laid at his door. His escapes were marvellous. However, through the efforts of Jonathan Wild, the celebrated thief-catcher, Jack was arrested and brought to trial. The jury never left their box and

their verdict was guilty. He was confined to Newgate awaiting execution, but after receiving two women visitors he escaped. Inside of two months he was back again, lodged
in a stone cell and chained to the floor. Again he escaped but his freedom was of short
duration. The law caught up with him and he stepped from the tail end of the hangman's
cart, at Tyburn on November 16, 1724, into eternity. For the thrilling details of his
escapes one should consult any chapbook history of this daring young personage, who was
only twenty-three when he died.

        Another public enemy of the past was Dick Turpin, who started out as a butcher's
apprentice but who was discharged "for the brutaility and egregious impropriety of his
conduct." He stole oxen and consorted with a gang of thieves which robbed smugglers,
stole deer, robbed churches and numerous homes, and placed their victims on hot grates
to force them to reveal the hiding places of their valuables. This gang built a secret
cave on the Waltham side of Epping, and finally acquired horses. Travelers were way-
laid and numerous robberies continued, accompanied by brutality. Rewards were issued
for the arrest of members of the band and all England was aroused. For several years
the gang lived in the cave, and then Turpin made the mistake of robbing a Mr. Major,
who was riding a one-time famous race-horse, White Stocking, of his mount. This was a
well-known horse and in due time Mr. Major got news of such an animal having been seen
at the Red Lion in Whitechapel. This led to an attempt to capture Turpin and his companion King, but in the battle, Turpin accidentally shot King and escaped. King later
died. The robberies continued but Turpin managed to keep out of the clutches of the
law. About 1736 Turpin assumed the name of Palmer and settled at Welton as a well-to-
do horse dealer. Through the shooting of one of his landlord's cocks in a fit of anger,
Palmer landed in jail and then strange facts began to come out about him. His explana-
tions were checked and found to be untrue. It was found that he had been arrested for
sheep stealing and had escaped. Finally he was moved to York Castle to await further
developments and in some way it came out that he was the notorious Dick Turpin. And so
he came to his end at the end of a rope, on April 7, 1739, at the age of thirty-three.
Once upon a time the account of this notorious highwayman could have been purchased for
a penny, or for sixpence if you wanted a chapbook bound in blue wrappers, and with an
engraved frontispiece showing Turpin at work on a hold-up.

Chapter 23

OF CHAPBOOKS UPON MISCELLANEOUS SUBJECTS

Many chapbooks were published upon subjects other than those covered in the foregoing chapters, as for example those upon social satire, matrimony, manners, customs, proverbs and so forth. From such chapbooks one could obtain information upon the most exact way of wooing a maid or a widow, on the way to write passionate love letters, or on the art of getting beautiful children, on the pleasures of matrimony, on the duties of a nursery maid, upon the delights of the bottle, upon the marriage ceremonies of various countries and upon the pleasures of a single life. And there were other informative ones also, explaining the vices of the age, supplying bon mots and proverbs, telling how to write witty and delightful letters, and dissecting Masonry.

Servants must have found "The coachman's and footman's catechism" very handy. In addition it contained, "Also an account of Betty the cook maid, Mary the kitchen maid, butler, and steward, porter gardner, postillion and groom, house keeper, house maid, chamber maid, laundry maid, nursery maid, and that sweet pretty creature call'd the lady's woman, that will really tell a hundred and fifty lies while she is dressing her lady; pray what is that for, but to turn the servants out of their places, and beg a silk gown now and then with ruffle cuffs to it and their three story church steeple maccaroni cap."

Some of the chapbooks of this group were in verse as well as in prose. W. Downing of London published in 1720, a merry poem called "The delights of the bottle; or, The compleat vintner; with the humours of bubble upstarts, stingy wranglers, dinner spungers, jill tiplers, beef beggars, cook teasers, pan soppers, plate twirlers, table whitlers, drawer biters, spoon pinchers. and other tavern torments."

Hodgson & Co., of London, brought out a twenty-four-page chapbook that sold for sixpence on "Horrid Customs or, An Afflicting Narrative relative to the Burning of Hindoo Widows on the Funeral Piles of their deceased Husbands; developing Numerous Instances of Dreadful Cruelty, and Female Devotion." Various instances as reported by eye-witnesses seem to have been collected for this chapbook and in the preface, it is stated that the number of Hindoo widows who were burnt or buried with their husbands had increased from 378 in 1815 to 839 in 1818.

In Paisley, G. Caldwell published "A Collection of Scotch Proverbs containing all the Wise Sayings and observations of the old people of Scotland, by Allan Ramsay." These are arranged alphabetically and include the following:

"A blate cat makes a proud mouse.
"A liar shou'd hae a good memory.
"A torchless dame sits lang at hame.
"It is needless to pour water on a drown'd mouse.
"Never shaw your teeth unless you can bite.
"There is life in a mussel as lang as she cheeps.
"Three can keep a secret if two be awa.
"When wine sinks words swim.
"Your head will never fit your father's bonnet."

"The Fashionable Letter Writer or, Ladies' and Gentlemen's Art of Polite Correspondence" sets forth the type of correspondence that should take place between a gentleman and a widow, a servant-man and his sweetheart, a daughter and her mother, a tenant and his landlord, a tradesman and a customer and other hypothetical persons. A daughter, for example, if away at school and subjected to inconveniences of one sort or another should write to her mother in the following vein:

"My dear Mamma

Will, I hope, forgive this complaint when I secretly inform her of the cause. Though I confess myself frequently negligent, yet my governess's severity discomposes me in such a manner, that I am really incapable of attending to my work. I am frequently deprived of my breakfast - sometimes of my dinner - and have often gone supperless to bed, because I have not drunk large basins of camomile tea, which is so exceedingly obnoxious to me. If my dear mamma would remove me to another school, or prevail upon my governess to moderate her cruelty, my future conduct, I hope, will prove me, A Dutiful Daughter."

THE
FASHIONABLE
LETTER WRITER.

LONDON :
Printed and Published by A. Ryle & Co , 2 & 3,
Monmouth Court, Bloomsbury.

Figure 66

Title page of "The Fashionable Letter Writer."

And the mother should notify her daughter that such unwarrantable usage justified her immediate removal to another school.

Frequently the contents of chapbooks do not measure up to the expectations created by their titles. Such is the case with "Female Policy Detected, or, the Arts of Designing Women laid open; Containing distinct warnings to Young Men, Against The Arts of Women, With numerous notable examples of the mischief and miseries which attend their sensuality and pride." Here the author had an excellent opportunity to expose his devastating wit, if he had any, but instead we have a dreary exposition of the opinions of Aristotle, Plato, Diogenes and others together with examples of designing women drawn from history, all more or less unconvincing.

Of more interest is John Miller's cheap tract number 10, printed at Dunfermline in 1828, entitled, "Awful Phenomena of Nature! Boiling Fountains in Iceland; A visit to the Cataract of Niagara; (The greatest water-fall in the world) A late ascent to Mount Blanc; (The highest mountain in Europe.) and, State of London during the Plague." Of Niagara Falls, the author wrote, "This evening I went down with one of our party to view the cataract by moonlight. I took my favorite seat on the projecting rock, at a little distance from the brink of the fall, and gazed till every sense seemed absorbed in contemplation. - Although the shades of night increased the sublimity of the prospect and 'deepened the murmur of the falling floods', the moon in placid beauty shed her soft influence upon the mind, and mitigated the horrors of the scene. The thunders which bellowed from the abyss, and the loveliness of the falling element, which glittered like molten silver in the moonlight, seemed to complete, in absolute perfection, the rare union of the beautiful with the sublime."

CHEAP TRACTS, No. 10.

Awful Phenomena of Nature!

Boiling Fountains in Iceland;
A VISIT TO THE
Cataract of Niagara;
(The greatest water-fall in the world.)
A late ascent to Mount Blanc;
(The highest Mountain in Europe.)
AND,
State of London during the Plague.

DUNFERMLINE:
PRINTED AND SOLD BY JOHN MILLER.

1828.

Figure 67

Awful Phenomena of Nature.

In 1750 "The Laird o' Coul's Ghost" appeared in type and was immediately popular with the customers of the running stationers. It consists of, "A copy of several Conferences and Meetings that passed betwixt the Rev. Mr. Ogilvie, late Minister of the Gospel at Innerwick in East Lothian, and the Ghost of Mr. Maxwell, late Laird of Coul. As it was found in Mr. Ogilvie's closet after his Death, very soon after these Conferences." On February 3, 1722 at seven o'clock in the evening Mr. Ogilvie was riding up the Burial Road when he heard hoof beats behind him. Upon asking who was there a voice replied, "The Laird of Coul, be not afraid." Thinking some one was playing a trick upon him, Mr. Ogilvie hurled his cane at the man, but it flew from his hand and encountered no resistance. Upon conversing with the Laird of Coul, Mr. Ogilvie found that the Laird was familiar with certain of his conversations. Other conferences take place between Mr. Ogilvie and the Laird, who is really not the Laird of Coul, but his ghost, and although these are of a religious nature and of spirits, it finally comes out at the end of the account, that the ghost wants Mr. Ogilvie to correct certain dishonest acts that the Laird of Coul had engaged in during his lifetime, whereby the heirs of certain persons had been defrauded of money. But Mr. Ogilvie did not relish the idea of going to the Laird's widow and telling her of her late husband's villanies. How could he expect to be believed? No one would believe that he had talked to a ghost. Mr. Ogilvie died shortly after his last conference and nothing would have been known of his strange experience had not the manuscript been found in Mr. Ogilvie's closet after his death.

Wonderful things could happen in chapbooks. There was "The Remarkable Case of Sarah Mason, a young woman of twenty-three years of age, who is now in Hide-Park Hospital for a most strange and uncommon disorder, who was on the 20th of last month opened before a great number of the most eminent physicians and surgeons in London, and had a surprising monster taken from her, which had been growing within her three years." According to the chapbook, "It was, in form, much like a lizard, and of a nasty greenish colour. It had four legs, and had feet like an eagle's talons, having three claws on each foot; its mouth was very wide, but had four teeth, and those very small. Its length from head to tail, measured full twenty-three inches, and was sixteen inches round. When it was put into the machine, which was prepared to hold it in, it flew about, and beat itself with such violence that it died in about an hour after it was taken out." Believe it or not.

Relating to marriage we have, "The Fifteen Comforts of Matrimony, or a looking-glass for all those who have enter'd in that holy and comfortable state, wherein are sum'd up all those blessings that attend a married life," printed in London in 1706, and another curious twenty-four-page book called, "John Thompson's Man: or a short Survey of the Difficulties and Disturbances that may attend a married life: to which are added some very extensive and most salutary Observations thereon; with certain and approved Rules for the choice of a Wife." The author's style is inclined to be somewhat Rabelaisian as may be seen from the following quotation. "16thly. If you would wed an old mapsie, murlie, mupit, crouch-backed, milk-mow'd, wirlie-faced, nipped, deformed creature to be thy wife, it is surely more out of love to her gear than herself; but as the proverb says, need makes naked men run, and sorrow makes websters spin, for it is her money renders her as nimble as an eel, and clouts all her broken clampers; but consider, it is often observed that you leave behind you the products of the soil, which is crook-backed, heckle-headed, midge-winged, mifly-kited, lap-lugged, ill-haired, bestranged, flat-nosed, bow-legged, squint-eyed, chandlerchafted, sheavel-gabbed, left-handed, craik-tailed, yellow-wamed, button-footed, beetle-boided, wap-nobbed, tanny-checked, rap-shanked, fiddle-flanked, tout-mon'd, antick, apish, ugly, saucy, infirmed, diseased, donard, doited, decriped, disjointed, distracted, distorted, weazel-faced, quarter-witted, punch-lipped, horn-hiped, ham-houghed, hair-brained, nonsensical, fantastical, goose-capical, coxcomical, and idiotical world's wonder, bursen-body, not only to possess your estate, but to build up your family - a pretty man indeed! And if these be help-meets let the world judge. So I think it is better for a man to live alone (if he lives a pious, chaste, virtuous, and honest life) than to be joined to one who will put him out of himself; for marriage, as it was said before, was designed for love, peace, and concord, and to be help-meets to each other; but as the proverb says, maidens are so meek till they be married, that men never so much as dream of a toolzie till the tocher come a-paying."

Still another matrimonial chapbook is, "The Pleasures of Matrimony, interwoven with sundry comical and delightful stories, with the charming delights and ravishing sweets of wooing and wedlock in all its diverting enjoyments." This contains some curious accounts of marriage ceremonies.

For love-letter writing, one could consult "The Delightful New Academy of Compliments, being the most exact art of wooing a maid, or widow, by way of dialogue, or complimental expressions. With passionate love letters, courtly sentences to express the elegance of love, and posies for gloves and rings. To which is added a choice collection of the newest songs sung at court and city, set by the best wits of the age." The following is a sample passionate love letter.

"Dear Madam, - Since I first beheld your bright eyes, they, like two blazing stars, have influenced wars and tumults in my soul, and banished rest from my abode. I have long stifled my flame, divinest creature, but at last it hath broke out to let you know how much I suffer, and that nothing but your smiles and condescending goodness can relieve me. Therefore begging life at your hands I cast myself, in imitation at your feet, prostrate at your feet; and in hopes of a favourable sentence, remain, madam, your most passionate and obedient servant, &c."

The various "cries" of London, of Banbury, and other places, with their quaint illustrations, belong in this group. Many of these were no doubt published exlusively for children, but they have delighted many old children for years, either as broadsides or chapbooks or as engravings.

> Here's cherries, oh! my pretty maids,
> My cherries round and sound;
> Whitehearts, Kentish, or Blackhearts
> And only twopence a pound.
>
> ———
>
> Here I am with my rabbits
>   Hanging on my pole,
> The finest Hampshire rabbits
>   That e'er crept from a hole.
>
> ———
>
> Now ladies here's roots for your gardens,
> Come buy some of me if you please,
> There's tulips, heart's-ease, and roses,
> Sweet William, and sweet peas.
>
> ———
>
> Old chairs to mend! Old chairs to mend!
> If I'd as much money as I could spend,
> If I'd as much money as I could spend,
> I'd leave off crying, "Old chairs to mend!"

Chapter 24

AMERICAN CHAPBOOKS

During Colonial and later times peddling was an active way of selling things. Although the peddler's stock during Colonial times was limited, by about 1830 it included all sorts of merchandise. Pins, scissors, razors, lace, perfume, cotton goods, pottery, spices, clocks, books and many other small articles were hawked about the countryside by peddlers, who slept in barns, or in taverns that catered to such trade. The peddlers were an adventuresome crew. They understood human nature and were versed in the arts of flattery and trade. Timothy Dwight in 1823 observed that many young peddlers parted early with modesty and principle and acquired cunning and coarse impudence. No doubt they needed these characteristics in order to stay in their chosen occupation. Most of the peddlers came from New England, especially Connecticut, and in addition to visiting homes, they were on hand at fairs, market days in towns, and at auction sales.

Some early peddlers specialized in broadsides turned out by Colonial printers. All sorts of events were celebrated in such accounts. The first peddlers of printed wares carried broadsides and popular books, and when religious books were distributed in that way, the peddler, of course, became a good influence. Some carried chapbooks, primers, catechisms, bibles, psalm books and various religious pamphlets and eventually we had book agents. Thousands of copies of the New England Primer were peddled throughout New England and were also sold in shops and general stores. As most of the printed matter of early days was of a religious nature, it follows that such publications, as were sold by peddlers, were largely of that type also. After about 1750, books on spelling, geography, grammar, palmistry, treatises on farming, almanacs, joke books, abbreviated legendary romances, and pamphlets on curious subjects, etc., began to appear, and the numbers of religious books suffered an increasing dilution.

There were numerous Colonial pamphlets on piety, goodness, sin, sermons, gospel, worship, doctrines, heaven, memorials, funeral sermons, prayers and sinners, and toward the end of the Colonial period titles appeared on the duty of parents, merchandizing of slaves, cultivation of flax, duty, health, currency and government, and there were also almanacs. Later, as 1800 was approached, the religious titles were diluted still more by other subjects. Except for a very few, such tracts cannot be classified as chapbooks.

The American Tract Society made use of special peddlers or colporteurs of their own, and by 1856 this organization had in its employ over 500 such agents who travelled through the country on foot, by horseback, wagon, boat, etc., selling tracts, bibles, religious works and similar literature.

Probably the best known book peddler was Parson Weems, the inventor of the George Washington cherry-tree tale, who from 1795 until his death in 1825 disseminated himself, his own works, and many of Mathew Carey's imprints into many rural and urban areas between New York and Georgia. A student of medicine, an ordained and one of the most active clergymen of Maryland, he took to the road and did his combined preaching and book selling on the steps of courthouses, in ballrooms, in the parlors of inns, on village commons and in the cottages of workers. He sold Bibles, children's books, historical and philosophical works, hymn books, prayer books and of course his own biographies, sermons, and moral pamphlets of his own publication. Some of Mason Locke Weems' moral pamphlets deserve to be classed as chapbooks because of their title pages and contents, although they are not so considered, because in the main they do not partake of other general chapbook characteristics. What could be more enticing than "The

Drunkard's Looking Glass. Reflecting a faithful likeness of the drunkard, in sundry very interesting attitudes, with lively representations of the many strange capers which he cuts at different stages of his disease," or "God's Revenge Against Adultery. Awfully exemplified in the following cases of American Crim. Con." The cases are those of Dr. Theodore Wilson of Delaware who seduced Mrs. Nancy Wiley and had his brains blown out by the lady's husband, and of the elegant James O'Neal of North Carolina who seduced Miss Matilda L'Estrange and was killed by Matilda's brother. And there is "Hymen's Recruiting Sergeant. Or the New Matrimonial Tat-too for the Old Bachelors. With some Elegant Songs." As a matter of fact the views of Parson Weems on marriage, drink, and adultery, bellowed through the pages of his pamphlets, are highly diverting, much more so than the contents of many chapbooks. Although designed as moral tracts, and sold for more than a few pennies, and printed in "handsome style" with frontispieces and engravings, I hereby nominate them for inclusion in the field of American chapbook literature as outstanding and unique contributions.

The Colonial presses of America issued many broadsides and it was natural that such types of English sheets should appear in America. At the beginning they were concerned with civil and religious proclamations, usually in prose, because verse was not in favor, but as time went on their subjects included funeral memorials, dying confessions, crime news and warnings, war-time ballads, marching songs, New Year's greetings, a few romantic ballads, admonitions, important events, local incidents, etc., all in crude verse. At first these had a distinct English flavor, and there was little that was original about them, but as time went on they acquired an American flavor and became less affected by English models. American broadside verse, however, never developed into literature either from poetical or metrical standpoints. The colonial pioneer atmosphere was not conducive to balladry. These American broadsides of from 1639 to 1800 with their grotesque, woodcut illustrations, lost contact with American life after the Revolution due to being crowded out by the newspaper. Although they persisted for some years, their authenticity of former days was gone.

One might assume that, along with the decline of broadsides in America, the chapbook era came into being, as a natural, subsequent period during which a certain type of cheap literature was supplied before the advent of cheap magazines and more newspapers, but there never was a chapbook era in America and chapbooks never achieved anything like the popularity here that they did in Great Britain. After the Revolution there was increased activity in magazines, but what is more important, the number of weekly and daily newspapers increased. Although newspapers did not print the kind of reading matter found in chapbooks, they, together with almanacs, printed sermons, etc., furnished a type of cheap reading matter that, while not replacing chapbook literature, did occupy the attention of the inhabitants. Another reason for the failure of chapbooks to flourish in America, was that the population had gotten beyond the elementary tastes and child-like intelligence required for the enjoyment of such works.

During the first century of colonization the culture of the inhabitants was European. There was practically no literature and Protestant ideas were dominant. Industry and thrift were important and idleness and pleasure were frowned upon. Work and worship were held up as pleasing to God. The use of tobacco in public, the wearing of lace, silk, and gold ornaments were forbidden. Card playing was illegal, people were whipped for blasphemy, lovers were fined for sitting under trees on Sundays, dancing to wanton ditties was condemned, amusement was looked upon with suspicion. In such an atmosphere there was little room for chapbooks, or for unreal or fantastical ideas.

However, it should not be assumed that there were no American chapbooks. Many American ones were reproduced from English originals, and some were typically American, but they were not printed and circulated in enormous numbers and they never achieved widespread popularity or became an important part of American culture. Examples of some of the American chapbooks that have come down to us are mentioned in the following pages.

Under the date, September 27, 1713, Cotton Mather wrote in his Dairy, "I am informed that the Minds and Manners of many people about the Countrey are much corrupted by foolish Songs and Ballads, which the Hawkers and Peddlars carry into all parts of the Countrey." As a remedy he suggested the widespread distribution of poetical compositions, full of piety.

Boston was an important centre for the printers and publishers of broadside and chapbook literature and many of the leading printers such as T. and J. Fleet, Andrew Barclay, and Isaiah Thomas produced chapbooks.

Fowle and Draper of Boston around 1755 kept large supplies of ballads and small books on hand for the numerous peddlers of that time. And Isaiah Thomas, who later became famous as a printer, publisher of children's books and as an antiquarian, was apprenticed to Zechariah Fowle, in 1755.

The Coverlys (1770-1822) a family of traveling newspaper publishers and journeyman printers, were responsible for the publication of numerous broadsides, ballad and otherwise. Nathaniel Coverly was operating in Boston in 1770, Chelmsford, 1774, Concord, 1776, Boston, 1779-1785, in partnership with Robert Hodge, in Plymouth, and in Boston again in 1788. In Amherst (N.H.) in 1795, the name of the firm was N. Coverly & Son. Nathaniel Coverly had two sons, Nathaniel and John and both sons were apparently printing in Salem from 1799 to 1803. In 1805 N. Coverly, Jr., was in Boston.

Andrew Steuart of Philadelphia printed chapbooks in 1763 and 1765, and it is fairly certain that he imported chapbooks from abroad for sale in America, some of them probably coming from James Magee of Belfast, Ireland. One of Steuart's chapbooks entitled "A Royal Old Song; containing the Life and tragical End of Fair Rosamund, Who was the concubine to King Henry, the Second, and put to death by Queen Elenor, in the famous Bower of Woodstock, near Oxford. To which is added, The Northern Lass," was printed in Philadelphia in 1763 and on the title page, he states that he has hundreds of different ballads for sale.

Another Steuart chapbook, printed in Philadelphia in 1765 is entitled, "The Undutiful Daughter or, the Devonshire Wonder," etc. The balance of the title describes the daughter of a widow, who took to an evil life and drank and swore and scoffed at her aged mother, to say the least. She had a child by a Mr. Lawrence and murdered the infant in a barn. She spent her mother's substance and sold herself to the devil, bewitched her husband and mother in a dreadful manner, was visited by ministers who prayed with her, and was finally executed. This sordid account is in verse.

Before the advent of the publications of the various tract societies, the religious chapbooks were solemn and heavy. Henry Miller, of Philadelphia, printed some of these in 1767, such as "The Emptiness and Vanity of A Life Spent in the Pursuit of Wordly (sic) Profit, Ease or Pleasure compared with A Life Wholly employed in endeavoring to glorify God, and do good to Mankind. Illustrated in An Extract of the Life and Death of the pious Lady Elizabeth Hastings. With Some Remarks on the Universality of the Love of God to Mankind," and "Daily Conversations with God, Exemplified in the Holy Life of Armelle Nicolas, A poor ignorant Country Maid in France, commonly known by the Name of The Good Armelle, Deceas'd in Bretaigne in the Year 1671." Both are sixteen pages in length, without illustrations, and the latter was printed from a London edition.

"The Friar and Boy: or, the young Piper's pleasant Pastime. Containing the witty Adventures betwixt the Friar and Boy, in relation to his Step Mother, whom he fairly fitted for her unmerciful cruelty," was printed and sold by A. Barclay, Boston, in 1767. This twenty-four page chapbook with its two woodcut illustrations was copied from a popular English version of the same title. The first English version was printed by Wynkyn de Worde.

Another chapbook subject printed as a broadside about 1770 by Thomas and John Fleet and sold at the Heart & Crown in Cornhill, Boston, was, "The Children in the Woods.

Being A true Relation of the inhuman Murder of two Children of a deceased Gentleman in
Norfolk, whom he left to the Care of his Brother; but this wicked Uncle, in order to get
the Childrens Estate, contrived to have them destroyed by two Ruffians, whom he had
hired for that Purpose," etc. This also is of English origin.

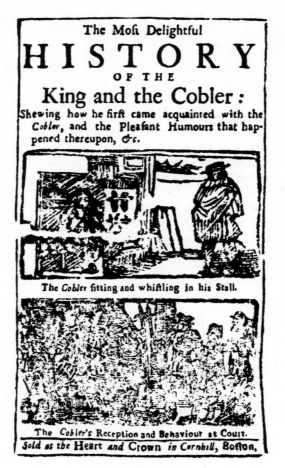

Figure 68

"The Most Delightful History of the King and the Cobler,"
published by Thomas and John Fleet of Boston.
(Courtesy of Dr. A. S. W. Rosenbach)

Thomas and John Fleet also published a sixteen-page chapbook on "The Most Delightful History of the King and the Cobler," etc. This story was popular in England
and numerous chapbook editions of it were printed.

About 1771 Isaiah Thomas at his printing office near the Mill Bridge in Boston,
printed and sold "The Prodigal Daughter," etc., a sixteen-page production in verse, and
this is illustrated by six woodcuts by Thomas, before he became the noted publisher of
children's books in Worcester.

In the "Boston Gazette and Country Journal" of January 20, 1772, the Boston
booksellers, Cox and Berry, advertised, "Little Books for the Instruction and Amusement
of all good Boys and Girls," and their notice included such titles as "The Cries of London," "History of Tom Jones," "History of Pamela," "History of Clarissa," the latter all
abridged, of course.

Some of the stories relating to the adventures of men, women and children who were captured by the Indians, were crudely printed in pamphlets of twenty-four pages, more or less, sometimes illustrated with woodcuts and sold by Yankee peddlers at isolated farmhouses, as well as by booksellers in towns. Such "captivities," as they are now called, should, I think, be classed as chapbooks. They represent a typical American contribution to chapbook literature. By this I do not mean to include all narratives of adventure and hardship relating to Indian captives, but only such as were published in typical chapbook style, sometimes with frontispieces and woodcuts, and sometimes subject to all the liberties that chapbook publishers usually took with their texts.

The chapbook editions for the most part began to appear shortly after the Revolution and were still being published in the 1870's, although peddlers at that time carried little in the way of literature. Various publishers and printers in New York, Boston, Philadelphia, Greenfield, Brooklyn, Elizabethtown, Hartford, Jaffrey (N.H.), Bridgeport, etc., brought out these chapbook captivities and some even appeared before 1776. Fowle and Draper of Boston printed one in 1760, and another Boston captivity appeared in 1748. After the Revolution they appeared in greater numbers from presses in New England and along the Atlantic seaboard. Along about 1840, editions were printed in such cities as Louisville, Kentucky and St. Louis, Missouri. A few publishers in London, Glasgow, Stirling and several other British cities brought out chapbook or abbreivated varieties of Indian captivities between such dates as 1760 and 1830. More detailed information relative to the publishers and dates of some of these chapbooks may be found in the catalogue (and its supplement) of the Ayer collection in the Newberry

THE
PRODIGAL DAUGHTER;

Or a ſtrange and wonderful relation, ſhewing, how a Gentleman of a vaſt Eſtate in BRISTOL, had a proud and diſobedient Daughter, who becauſe her parents would not ſupport her in all her extravagance, bargained with the Devil to poiſon them. How an Angel informed her parents of her deſign. How ſhe lay in a trance four days ; and when ſhe was put in the grave, ſhe came to life again, &c. &c.

BOSTON, printed and ſold at I. THOMAS's Printing-Office near the MILL BRIDGE.

Figure 69

Title page of "The Prodigal Daughter," published
by Isaiah Thomas in Boston, about 1771
(Courtesy of Dr. A. S. W. Rosenbach)

Library in Chicago, and also from the collections of captivities in the American Antiquarian Society, Library of Congress, New York Public Library, and the John Carter Brown Library.

In 1824 James E. Seaver's "A Narrative of the Life of Mrs. Mary Jemison," was published and this was used as the basis for a chapbook edition by Asher Wright who is supposed to have edited and published the first abridgment entitled, "Interesting Narrative of Mary Jemison, who lived nearly seventy-eight years among the Indians, Buffalo, 1834." This edition was reprinted, sometimes with a folding plate, by various firms in Rochester, Utica, Westfield, etc., from 1840 to as late as 1871.

Typical chapbook titles introduced the narratives to the readers. Sometimes they were short and sometimes they were as long as the longest chapbook titles. For example, there was "The affecting history of dreadful distresses of Frederick Manheim's family. To which are added, an encounter between a white man and two savages. Adventures of Capt. Isaac Stewart. Deposition of Mary Herbeson. Adventures and suffering of Peter Williamson. Remarkable adventures of Jackson Johonnot. Account of the destruction of the settlements at Wyoming. Printed for Chapman Whitcomb," [1792-1793], who was a New England peddler and publisher of many similar chapbooks. In Boston there appeared, in 1748, "A narrative of the captivity of Nehemiah How, who was taken by the Indians at the Great Meadow-Fort above Fort Dummer, where he was an inhabitant, October 11th, 1745. Giving an account of what he met with in his travelling to Canada, and while he was in prison there. Together with an account of Mr. How's death at Canada."

Josiah Priest, who was born at Unadilla, N.Y., in 1788 and who died at Enes, N.Y., in 1851, was, in addition to being a coach-trimmer and harness maker, an historian of the American frontier and his writings included Indian captivities, some of which belong to the chapbook type. He started his literary work about 1824 and his works appear to have been published between 1825 and 1844. He wrote to sell and of the thousands of his Colonial and Revolutionary War pamphlets, few original copies have survived. An interesting account of Priest and a bibliography of his productions by W. H. Duncan was recently printed in the Proceedings of the American Antiquarian Society.

It should be stated that some of the captivities or early thrillers were published even earlier than the dates previously mentioned, but the original editions of these works are exceedingly scarce. One of the earliest is "Mary Rowlandson's Captivity," first published at Cambridge, Massachusetts, in 1682. There were others, some of which went into numerous editions. Some were very popular, especially those dealing with such captives as Peter Williamson, Mary Jemison, and Benjamin Gilbert. The Indians were the greatest kidnappers of all times and their victims were of all ages. If young and healthy they were adopted by the tribes. The accounts of the sufferings and hardships endured by the captives, were popular with, and thrilling to, many of our ancestors and such of these pamphlets as have survived show some of the difficulties that beset our pioneers and are now the sources of many historical facts.

A one-time popular, but now rare, captivity narrative was called, "A very surprising narrative, of a young woman, discovered in a rocky-cave, after having been taken by the savage Indians of the wilderness, in the year 1777, and seeing no human being for the space of nine years. In a letter from a gentleman to his friend." This was written under the pseudonym Abraham Panther and various editions were published under the above title or variations of it, in New York, Windsor, Greenfield, Putney, Augusta, Leominster, Bennington, etc., from about 1786 to about 1816. In this narrative, two travelers on a journey through the western wilderness discover to their inexpressible amazement, "a most beautiful young Lady sitting near the mouth of a cave." This young lady was singing and did not see the two visitors until a dog barked and warned her of their approach. Upon seeing them, she screamed and then fainted dead away. But she soon recovered and exclaimed, "Heavens! Where am I? And who, and from whence are you?" After some conversation and after being convinced that no harm would come to her, she told her sad story. Born near Albany, in 1760, she was the only child of a father of some consequence and considerable estate. However, when she was but fifteen, one of her father's clerks, a young man of easy politeness, good sense and agreeable manners, found his way to her heart and his ardour was reciprocated. Their attachment to each other was concealed from her father because he was so busy in the pursuit of riches, and the lovers had no reason to suppose that he would look with favor upon the marriage of his daughter to one destitute of fortune. Eventually the father discovers the love affair and after discharging the young man from his employ and after a scene in which he upbraids his daughter, he orders her confined to her chamber. The separated lovers manage, through an old servant, to correspond with each other and an elopement is planned. The young lady packs her clothes, and leaves her father's house on the evening of May 10, 1777, destined to meet her lover in a little hut in the country. The father organizes a searching party and the lovers abandon the hut and move further into the country. However, a horrid scene followed. They were surrounded and made prisoners by a party of Indians who barbarously murdered the girl's lover, cutting and mangling him in the most inhuman manner and burning him at the stake while they danced around and rejoiced in their brutal cruelty.

The young girl eluded her guard and finally after wandering for fourteen days, being supplied by day "by the spontaneous produce of the earth," and sleeping on the ground by night "with the canopy of heaven" for her covering, she was captured by a gigantic Indian who led her to a cave and gave her food. After spurning his advances, she was bound and given the night to decide between his proposal or death. Happily, she was able to bite through her bonds of walnut bark and knowing that she could not hope to escape by flight, in her own words, - "I did not long deliberate but took up the hatchet he had brought and, summoning resolution I, with three blows, effectually put an end to his existence."

"I then cut off his head and next day, having cut him in quarters, drew him out of the cave about half a mile distant, when, after covering him with leaves and bushes, I returned to this place. I now found myself alone, in possession of this cave in which are several apartments. I here found a kind of Indian corn which I planted and have yearly raised a small quantity. Here I contented myself as well as my wretched situation would permit; here have I existed for nine long years, in all which time this faithful dog which I found in the cave has been my only companion and you are the only human beings who ever heard me tell my tale."

The travelers finally took the lady to her father's home where there was a touching reunion during which the old gentleman fainted. Upon recovering he insisted upon hearing at once of his daughter's experience, as he had but a few minutes to live. After this and after asking forgiveness, he fell into another faint from which he never recovered. And he left a handsome fortune to his daughter.

This, according to Mr. Vail is, in all likelihood, not a bona fide captivity, but probably a piece of early American fiction disguised as fact in order to be acceptable to a public unused to fiction.

Isaiah Thomas in 1786 published in Worcester, the popular title, "A Wonderful Discovery of a Hermit, Who lived upwards of two hundred years." This is a twelve-page chapbook with a cut of Robinson Crusoe on the title page. This particular hermit was formerly a citizen of London who became involved with a nobleman's daughter and had to leave the country. He sailed for Italy in 1580, but was shipwrecked and finally ended in a cave back of the Virginia mountains where he was discovered by two gentlemen in June, 1785. This popular broadside and chapbook account was printed by Ezekiel Russell of Boston, Daniel Bowen of New Haven, George Jerry Osborne of Portsmouth, Woodward and Green of Middletown, Joseph Hall of Pittsburg, and John Trumbull of Norwich, all in 1786, according to their imprints. The account is attributed to James Buckland and John Fielding, the two men who discovered him.

Such titles as "The Death and burial of Cock Robin" and "The House that Jack built," were printed by W. Spotswood of Philadelphia in 1786; "The facetious history of

John Gilpin," by George Jerry Osborne of Newburyport, in 1793, Wrigley & Berriman of Philadelphia, in 1794, and by J. Dunham of Hanover, in 1794. Daniel Bowen of New Haven, printed "A Collection of funny, moral, and entertaining stories and bon-mots," in 1787, and in the same year Peter Brynberg of Wilmington brought out "The History of Jane Shore, and Fair Rosamond." "The World turned upside down" was published by Walters and Norman of Philadelphia in 1779, "Whittington and his cat," by Moses H. Woodward of Middletown in 1790, and "The Children in the Wood," by J. Babcock of Hartford in 1796.

A

NARRATIVE

OF THE

SUFFERINGS,

A N D

Surprizing DELIVERANCE

O F

WILLIAM *and* ELIZABETH FLEMING,

Who were taken captive by Capt. *Jacob*, Commander of the *Indians*, who lately made an Excursion on the Inhabitants of the *Great-Cove*, near *Conecocheig*, in *Pennsylvania*, as related by themselves.

Pfalm iii. 4. *I cried unto the Lord, and he heard me.*

PHILADELPHIA:

Printed by *James Chattin*, for the Benefit of the unhappy Sufferers. 1756. *Price 6d.*

Figure 70

Title page of an "Indian Captivity,"
published in Philadelphia in 1756.
(Courtesy of New York Public Library.)

The popular English "Berkshire Lady," in verse appeared in Philadelphia in 1790 as an eight-page chapbook and Henry Green of Philadelphia printed "Death and the Lady. To which is added The Bride's Burial" about the same time. The familiar ballad, "The Babes in the Wood. Their Death and Burial" was printed as an eight-page chapbook in Philadelphia in 1791 and Daniel Lawrence of the same city, about 1792, printed "The History of Joseph and his Brethren: Wherein we may behold the wonderful Providence of God, in all their Troubles and Advancements," in sixteen pages of verse. A twenty-four-page illustrated chapbook entitled "The history of Dorastus and Faunia," etc., was printed by J. White of Boston in 1795 and no doubt its text followed an English chapbook version.

"The History of George Barnwell, of London," in twenty-two pages, appeared over the imprint of John Trumbull of Norwich, in 1792; John Byrne of Windham printed the

"Travels of Robinson Crusoe. Written by Himself" in 1792, in an illustrated thirty-two page edition; N. & J. Coverly of Salem printed "The Remarkable History of Tom Jones, a Foundling," in 1799, in thirty-two pages; and Nathan Douglas of Poughkeepsie printed a twelve-page chapbook in 1796, called, "The Two Babes in the Wood: Together with Divine Songs for Children." There were chapbooks on fortune telling also, as indicated by "The Fortune Teller," etc., printed by Francis Bailey of Philadelphia in 1793, in fifty-six pages.

Tiebout of New York published a fat 110-page chapbook, illustrated by crude woodcuts in 1796, entitled "The History of Fair Rosamund, Mistress to Henry II, and Jane Shore, Concubine to Edward VI, Kings of England. Shewing how they came to be so; with their Lives, remarkable Actions, and unhappy Ends."

Little is on record of the individualities of native American chapmen, and it is a pleasure to record the eccentricities and some personal history of Chapman Whitcomb, who was not only a peddler of chapbooks, but a publisher of them as well.

Chapman Whitcomb, the third child of Asa Whitcomb, was born in Hardwick, Massachusetts, March 5, 1765. At the age of twenty, he graduated from Dartmouth College in the class of 1785. He was interested in literary pursuits and frequently indulged in eccentricities. It is recorded that when the young lady, whom he had unsuccessfully wooed, was married to his rival, he attended the wedding attired in a green suit. He must have gotten over his disappointment, for in 1793, he was married and living in the part of Harvard, Massachusetts, called Still River, where he eventually acquired property. Whitcomb was a perambulating teacher of grammar, or as it was called in his time, English. His clothing had enormous outside pockets in which he stuffed old rags, feathers, etc., which he later sold. And his income from teaching was supplemented also by the sale of chapbooks which were probably all printed for him at Leominster, Massachusetts, where Charles Prentiss and Salmon Wilder, with various associates, successfully ran a job-press from 1796 to 1813. Whitcomb also loaned money on real estate and did carpentering in a small way. At his death on March 22, 1833, his property was valued at about three thousand dollars.

The American Antiquarian Society at Worcester, Massachusetts, is the fortunate possessor of some nineteen or twenty of Chapman Whitcomb's chapbooks, which I had the pleasure of examining. The contents of these chapbooks are quite varied and represent religious and moral tales, biography, adventure, fiction, geography, and other topics. Sometimes Whitcomb's own productions appeared in chapbook form. For example his poem "Comparative View of Religion" that was published in his "Miscellaneous Poems" (Worcester, 1795) appeared in a twelve-page chapbook entitled "A concise view of antient and modern religion; With a letter, from a deformed gentleman to a young lady, who slighted him, &c. Printed for Chapman Whitcomb." Others of his religious chapbooks included the life of Judas Iscariot written by John Thompson and the lives of the apostles by J. Taylor.

"The farmer's daughter, of Essex. Being a history of the life and sufferings of Miss Clarissa Dalton. By William Pen. [James Penn] Printed for Chapman Whitcomb," appeared about 1810. This was a popular title with other publishers. Dean and Munday of London brought it out and it was printed by J. Babcock of Hartford, Conn., in 1797, by Jacob S. Mott in 1798, John C. Totten in 1814, and W. Borradaile in 1823, all of New York. "A present to Children. Consisting of several new divine hymns, moral songs & entertaining stories," another Whitcomb chapbook, was also printed by T. Green about 1740. Green conducted a printing business at New London, Conn., from about 1714 to 1757.

Whitcomb published "captivities" also. There was "A remarkable narrative of Mrs. Frances Scott, an inhabitant of Washington County, Virginia. Printed for Chapman Whitcomb" in sixteen pages, describing how the home of Mr. Scott was raided by the Indians in June, 1785. Mr. Scott and the children were killed. Mrs. Scott was carried off but was able to escape after eleven days, when she was left with the chief, an old man, while the others went in search of food. Mrs. Scott wandered in the wilderness

for thirty-one days before coming upon a settlement. Whitcomb also published, about
1799, the popular Abraham Panther captivity, in twelve pages, under the following title:
"A surprising narrative of a young woman, discovered in a cave in the wilderness, after
having been taken by the savage Indians, and seeing no human being for the space of nine
years, in a letter. By a gentleman to his friend. Leominster: Printed for Chapman
Whitcomb, By Charles Prentiss." And in addition he brought out the Mary Rowlandson and
Frederick Manheim captivities in chapbook form.

Other chapbooks published by Whitcomb were the Life of Moll Flanders, although
it is entitled "The Life of Poll Flanders," and it must have shocked some of his neighbors, "The crafty princess; or golden Bull," and "The history of Capt. Thomas Parismas,
containing a particular account of the cruel and barbarous treatment of a young lady,
who was the wife of Mr. James Negotio, a merchant, in the East Indies" etc., which according to the title page "would almost bring tears of blood, even to the eyes of a
Nero." This tale was also published at Medford, Massachusetts, in 1798.

CRAFTY PRINCESS;

or,

GOLDEN BULL.

IN FOUR PARTS.

Printed at LEOMINSTER, (Mass.)

Figure 71

Title page of "The Crafty Princess," published
and peddled by Chapman Whitcomb.

Like other chapbook publishers, Whitcomb was not averse to bringing out the same
account under different titles. Thus we find that his twelve pages of prose entitled
"Arguments in favor of the ladies; or an answer to the scurrilous invectives of those

who have a light esteem of them" is substantially the same as his chapbook called, "The
female character vindicated: Or an answer to the scurrilous invectives of fashionable
gentlemen:" In spite of what the title seems to promise, it is a rather dull, prosy account and contains the proverb

> A Father's a Father, till he gets a new wife,
> And a Mother's a Mother, all the days of her life.

"Geography epitomized. A short but comprehensive description of the terraque-
ous globe, in verse, to assist the memory. Printed for Chapman Whitcomb. With privi-
lege of copy right" published about 1796, in sixty pages, is an interesting example of
how geography was once taught in some places. Except for a short introduction in prose,
the entire account is in verse and the following, which is one of five verses describing Italy, illustrates the treatment that is used for all the countries of the globe.

> From the rough tow'ring Alps, if you venture so high,
> Whose tops, clad in snows, seems to blend with the sky;
> In prospect lies Italy, stretching south east,
> And there by a far-flowing sea is embrac'd.
> The Appenine Ridge this rich region divides,
> And many fine rivers roll down both its sides.
> In form, like a leg of vast size it extends,
> And Sicily rises, where Italy ends.

"A Full and Particular Narrative of the Life, Character and Conduct of John
Banks, A Native of Nieuport, in Austrian Flanders, who is to be executed on the 11th
day of July 1806, for the wilful murder of his wife Margaret Banks. To which is prefixed, A Correct Copy of his Trial & Condemnation, with an appendix containing His Confession, Voluntarily made by himself, in the presence of the Editor, attended by one of
the keepers, who (if required,) will testify to its truth. 'Whoso sheddeth man's
blood, by man shall his blood be shed.' - Holy Writ. New-York: Printed For The Proprietor. 1806."

This crime chapbook justified its existence in 1806 by stating in its preface
that, "one example is better than ten precepts," and that, "to hold the mirror up to
nature, and paint virtue and vice in their proper colour is the task of the moralist
and historian: and although a painful, yet it is a necessary duty to expose moral depravity, and point out its pernicious effects upon society." Some time after John
Banks arrived in New York, he married a very handsome young woman of twenty named Margaret Miller, with whom he lived ten months, and then cut her throat.

According to the chapbook account of the trial which reports the testimony of
different witnesses, he was impelled to do this because his wife was addicted to drunkenness, and was abusive and tantalizing in addition. As a matter of fact, he struck
her with a shovel and then "cut her throat from ear to ear by sawing with a razor until
he thought he had cut enough to kill her." For this he was sentenced to death and the
chapbook recounts his confession and the attitude he took before his execution. For
the most part he was unconcerned and anxious to have the whole thing end as soon as possible. Of course, toward the last he prayed every day and all night, but he continued
to have a good appetite. Toward the very last he lamented his crime and was overwhelmed with tears. However, just before his execution, he was placid and tranquil.
"After a short but very fervent prayer he stepped off the board, and spoke to the
sheriff - then stepping up again he took the rope out of his bosom, and fastened it to
the hook, adjusted the knot, and in about a minute drew the cap over his face; then
dropping his handkerchief as a signal was launched into eternity, at 1 o'clock precise-
ly."

Previously, troops were formed at the gate of the city prison to receive the
prisoner who was dressed in white, and barefoot. The procession moved in the following
order, first, a detachment of artillery, second, the sheriff, under-sheriff, etc., third,

a cart with a coffin, and a group of civil officers, fourth, the prisoner with his priest, fifth, more artillery.

Carlos C. Darling of Montpelier, Vermont, printed in 1807 a typical chapbook of twelve pages, bound in blue paper covers, entitled "The Devil and Doctor Faustus," which was copied in its entirety from an English chapbook. "The School of Good Manners" was published at Windsor, Vermont, in 1815.

"The Devil let loose; or a Wonderful instance of the goodness of God. Being the substance of a letter from a gentleman in South Carolina, to his friend in Annapolis, in Maryland. Though the wicked join hand in hand, yet they shall not go unpunished," was reprinted in twenty-four pages by C. Spear of Hanover, N.H., in 1814.

Nathaniel Coverly, of 16 Milk Street, Boston, printed in 1820, a blue paper-covered chapbook of twenty-four pages entitled, "Some particulars relative to John Fisher and Lavina Fisher, his Wife, who were executed at Charleston, S.C. Feb. 18, 1820. To which are added Remarks on crime and punishment, with other miscellaneous observations."

About 1828 in New York, there was published a thriller of thirty-six pages called, "Piratical Barbarity or the Female Captive. Comprising the particulars of the capture of the English Sloop Eliza-Ann and the horrid massacre of the unfortunate crew by the Pirates, March 12, 1825 and the unparalleled sufferings of Miss Lucretia Parker, a prisoner for eleven days."

Another hermit chapbook was published in Providence in 1829, entitled, "Early Life and Adventures of Robert Voorhis, the Hermit of Massachusetts, Who has lived 14 Years in a Cave, Secluded from Human Society." This has a curious woodcut frontispiece and the contents tell of his birth, sufferings and of his escape from cruel bondage in early life and of his reasons for becoming a recluse. This hermit was born in Princeton, N.J., in 1769, his mother being of African descent and his father being not only a pure, white-blooded Englishman, but a gentleman as well. Desiring freedom from slavery he placed his confidence in a villain named Bevins who hurried him aboard a schooner bound for Charleston, S.C., where he was placed in irons. He escaped, and also lost his wife and children.

There is no doubt that English chapbooks were imported and sold in this country just as were other books. William Williams, a printer of Utica, N.Y., in the "Patriot and Patrol," of August 18, 1818 advertised for the wholesale and retail trade, "8,000 Chap Books, 60 kinds," and "27,000 toy books, 33 kinds," and previous to that date there are booksellers' advertisements relating to definite importations from abroad.

In 1838 Smith and Carpenter of New York published "The Pennsylvania Hermit, a twenty-four page chapbook dealing as the title page states, "with the extraordinary life of Amos Wilson who expired in a cave in the neighborhood of Harrisburg, after having therein lived in solitary retirement for the space of nineteen years, in consequence of the ignominious death of his sister." Other editions appeared previous to 1838 and the Pennsylvania Hermit had a certain degree of popularity. Almost half of the text is devoted to Mr. Wilson's life by an unnamed biographer and the balance to an account, supposed to have been written by Mr. Wilson, on "The Sweets of Solitude or instructions to mankind, How They May Be Happy in a Miserable World." A frontispiece shows a sylvan scene and Amos Wilson attired in a flowing gown, reading the Bible, all faintly reminiscent of the woodcuts in Caxton's "Vitas Patrum."

It appears that Amos Wilson, who was born in Lebanon, Dauphin County, Pennsylvania, in 1774 had a younger sister named Harriot, who at the age of eighteen or nineteen was "deceived and shamefully seduced by a wretch" named Smith, a married man and a Philadelphian. The body of Miss Wilson's child was found and she was charged with murder, tried, and found guilty. Efforts on the part of leading citizens to obtain a pardon for her were without success until the day before the execution, when Amos Wilson's additional pleas softened the governor's heart. However, Amos did not reach the scene of the hanging in time. Delayed by a swollen river, he arrived five minutes too late and was a witness to his sister's dying struggles. For months afterward he was delirious, and upon recovering, he decided to withdraw from society. This he did by retiring to a cave twelve miles from Harrisburg, where he lived for nineteen years, making millstones, reading the Bible and other religious works, and writing. After his death about 1813, his friend and biographer found in a corner of the cave the manuscripts which Wilson had written and among them was "The Sweets of Solitude." This melancholic account of Amos and Harriot Wilson may or may not be true. Mr. Wilson's biographer, although reporting in some detail the exact time of the day that Miss Wilson ascended the gallows, the convulsive movements of her hands, etc., and moralizing at length upon the evils of departing from "dignified modesty" does not concern himself very much with names and dates. The chapbook is written in a somewhat ecclesiastical style and abounds in such terms as "distressing circumstances," "cruel fate," "ignominious death," "fond expectations," "vile seducer," "poor deluded female," "vale of tears," and vice and virtue are capitalized.

The "Sweets of Solitude" is a dissertation on the necessity of being "truly pious" in order to be "truly happy." The entire chapbook was probably written with the idea of stirring the emotions of the readers through the recital of the crime, and at the same time calling their attention to the desirability of leading a Christian life.

When Wiclif began to distribute his brief, hand-written thoughts on religious subjects, he started something that probably will never end so long as printing presses, paper and populations endure. The invention of printing greatly facilitated what Wiclif had originated, and with the general interest in religion, it was only a question of time until Christian literature was being generally distributed in tract form. Various tract societies were formed. In England, the Society for Promoting Christian Knowledge was incorporated in 1701. Later John Wesley published tracts and organized the Society for Promoting Religious Knowledge among the Poor, and similar societies sprang up in other places. Toward the end of the century Hannah More's Cheap Repository Tracts began to circulate, designed in part to counteract the supposed evil effects of the inelegant chapbooks, and in 1799 the well-known Religious Tract Society of London was organized.

In this country the pioneers were the Methodist Book Concern, with its first publications in 1789; the Massachusetts Society for Promoting Christian Knowledge, founded in 1803; the New York Religious Tract Society, organized in 1812; the New England Tract Society, of Andover, in 1814, and Boston in 1823 under its new name, the American Tract Society; and the American Tract Society, New York, 1825, formed by a merger of the American Tract Societies of New York and Boston. Others of lesser fame and influence flourished also during these times.

Tracts still survive today, in spite of the large public interest in things other than religion. One may purchase an ounce, half-pound, or pounds of them, on subjects ranging from Afflictions, Appeal, Backsliders, and Conversion, to Temperance, Theatre, and Worldly Amusements. There are about ten eight-page tracts to an ounce, and the retail price is nine cents an ounce, thirty-five cents a quarter-pound, seventy cents a half-pound, and $1.40 a pound.

"The Dairyman's Daughter" was and probably still is a popular tract, although not a penny one. It first appeared when bowdlerized editions of Shakespeare were in vogue and when thrift and industry were esteemed and pleasure and idleness were lamented. Written by Rev. Legh Richmond, a native of Liverpool and published separately for the Religious Tract Society previous to 1814, it was in that year incorporated with other of Richmond's writings under the title "Annals of the Poor" which had a large circulation in England and abroad. Since then its popularity grew and grew and numerous editions were printed in various English and American cities. It is claimed that four million copies in nineteen languages had been circulated before the year 1849.

The tract itself, supposedly an authentic narrative, is concerned mainly with the visits of Rev. Richmond to a dairyman's cottage, his conversations with the dairyman's daughter, Elizabeth W----, a former servant girl, dying of consumption, the meditative and flattering letters that Elizabeth W---- sent to him, his own moralizing, and the burial services that he conducted for both Elizabeth and her sister. Mr. Richmond believed that ordinarily, religiousness and poverty went hand-in-hand, and that religion in a pure state was found only in the homes of the poor. And he changed the wording of Elizabeth's letters so that their thoughts and style could not be distinguished from his own. As for Elizabeth, her wickedness apparently consisted only in being thoughtless, fond of pretty clothes, and in neglecting her soul. During her illness, she became introspective and considered herself "as a brand plucked from the burning."

Various testimonials testified to the beneficial effects of reading "The Dairyman's Daughter." These appeared in Tract 104 of the American Tract Society. In one instance a female servant, after reading it, "was deeply impressed with a sense of her sinful condition." In another case, a young lady after reading it, died nine months later, "in the happiest and most enlightened state of mind." And there are other records of converted servant girls. Although housemaids seemed to be quite susceptible to its influence, it was not impotent in other occupational groups, for a "gay, young officer in the Navy," after receiving a copy of "The Dairyman's Daughter" from a common sailor, became "deeply and affectionately serious."

The New England Tract Society was organized at Andover in 1814. In 1823 it moved to Boston and changed its name to the American Tract Society. Two years later it became merged in the American Tract Society that was organized in New York on May 11, 1825. The New York Religious Tract Society, many of whose publications were printed by D. Fanshaw of 20 Slote-Lane and which probably existed before 1824, was, I think, incorporated with the American Tract Society in 1825. These tract societies all issued about the same type of moral and religious chapbooks, ranging from four to twenty-four pages, frequently with a woodcut on the first page, which served both as a cover and title page. They were concerned with Sabbath breaking, the evils of drunkenness, swearing, breaking laws, gambling, etc., the history of the Bible, happy poverty, the lives of poor and pious persons, the various commandments, the parable of the prodigal son, the broad and narrow paths, and short popular sermons.

The American Sunday School Union, an outgrowth of previous movements, was organized in Philadelphia in 1824 and many moral and religious chapbooks, or tracts, were published by this organization. At one time their "Depository" was located at 29 North Fourth Street, Philadelphia, and their publications were printed by such firms as Clark & Raser, and I. Ashmead & Co. Their eight to twelve-page chapbooks were always embellished with a woodcut on the title page and dealt with a variety of subjects including "The Death of an Infidel," "The Life of William Kelly; or, the Converted Drunkard," "The Swearer's Prayer," "The Pensioner and his Daughter Jane," and "John Elliot, the apostle to the American Indians." In "The Swearer's Prayer" various judgments that overtook swearers are cited, of which the following is an example.

"In the year 1806, Joseph Shepherd, an inhabitant of Bledlow, in the county of Bucks, remarkable for his depravity, drunkenness, profane cursing and swearing, and contempt of the gospel, was offered a pint of ale, upon condition of his damning the methodists. This proposal was so agreeable to his own wicked inclinations and habits, that he readily complied with it, and received the promised reward. But a more dreadful recompense was at hand! On Wednesday, October 1st, he was repeating at a public-house, his wishes for the damnation of those religious persons, generally called methodists, with horrid oaths, (too shocking to be expressed) when in about two hours afterwards, it pleased God suddenly to strike him with a mortal disease, which at its commencement, deprived him of the use of his hands and feet, (which was afterwards restored;) and so rapid was the progress of the disorder, as to put a period to his life on the Monday following."

Although the term chapbook should, I think, be restricted to cheap literature distributed by peddlers, it is not always possible to adhere to a hard and fast definition. This is especially true of children's chapbooks in America. Sometimes it is difficult to know whether a child's book is a chapbook or just a child's book. However, so far as possible, I prefer to classify as chapbooks for children such toy books as were sold for a penny or so by peddlers, or by booksellers and stationers in the towns and villages. In addition I think the contents should have amusing or entertaining qualities rather than instructive ones, although in many cheap toy books, the text was meant to be instructive as well as entertaining. These standards, which after all are somewhat personal, would exclude primers, spelling books, catechisms and the like, as well as the more expensive little books with engraved and colored plates.

Thomas White, a puritan minister, wrote for the benefit of children, "When thou canst read, read no ballads and romances and foolish books, but the Bible and the Plaine Man's Pathway to Heaven, a very plaine holy book for you," and in addition he mentioned other holy, but dull books. For the most part the books that Colonial children were supplied with were written by religious persons or ministers and their contents dealt with piety, death-bed scenes, sin, and records of religious precocity. And they were a dreary lot.

"Aesop's Fables," and "Reynard the Fox" circulated in chapbook form, but adventures, romance, and imagination were scarce in children's literature of the Colonial period. It was not until John Newbery, the English publisher, appeared on the scene, about 1744, that story books were published especially for children. Many of his books were imported into America, but few, if any, could really be called chapbooks. His children's books were more substantial and durable. They were bound and decorated and their contents were more suitable for young persons than the coarse tales found in chapbooks.

Isaiah Thomas, the printer and patriot, brought out after the Revolution many little books for children, some of which might be called chapbooks, and many of them were reprints of English books, especially those of John Newbery.

Many firms in New York, Philadelphia and Boston published what might be called chapbooks for children. As a rule they were about $3\frac{1}{2}$ or 4 inches high and about $2\frac{1}{2}$ inches wide with colored paper covers, and the number of their pages ran from eight to thirty-two or more. They were frequently illustrated with little pictures. On the other hand there was nothing fixed about their sizes and some were seven inches tall and four and a half inches wide.

They appeared in large numbers during the first half of the nineteenth century, in the cities mentioned above, and also in such cities as Albany, Baltimore, Concord, Hartford, New Haven, Worcester, Portland, Cooperstown and many other places. Frequently they were printed as side lines to more important printing activities, although there were a few firms that specialized in children's books, such as Isaiah Thomas of Worcester, Samuel Wood & Sons, Samuel King, and Mahlon Day of New York, the Babcocks of Hartford, Rufus Merrill of Concord, the Johnsons of Philadelphia, etc., and among their numerous productions are many that seem to meet the specifications of children's chapbooks.

The contents of these little books was quite variable. There were hymns, fables, histories of birds, beasts and insects, riddles, stories, easy lessons, wisdom in miniature, fairy tales, games, pictures, geography and scraps of information on this and that subject. Many were little moral tales on goodness, idleness, fidelity and vanity, but no doubt the children instinctively escaped the moralizing of their elders who wrote these books. Of course, the standard folk-tales, nursery rhymes and fairy tales all appeared in chapbook form for children, frequently with illustrations, plain and colored, and some of the textual variations in Jack and the Bean Stalk, Jack the Giant Killer, and others are quite startling and wonderful to behold.

B. & J. Johnson of Philadelphia about 1800 printed many of Hannah More's Cheap Repository Tracts that were so popular in England. It has been stated that William Cobbett was largely instrumental in their circulation in America. Jacob Johnson, a Quaker, established himself in the book business in Philadelphia at 147 Market Street about 1780, and became famous as a publisher of children's books. About 1808 he entered into a partnership with Benjamin Warner and the firm continued at the same place as Johnson and Warner. Twenty years later, the firm was taken over by M'Carty & Davis.

An elaborate thirty-two-page, illustrated "History of Whittington and his Cat" was published by Jacob Johnson in Philadelphia in 1802, and Turner & Fisher of New York and Philadelphia brought out a twenty-four-page chapbook about 1835 on "The History of Jack the Giant Killer, containing the whole of his wonderful exploits. Embellished with Ten Engravings."

Samuel King of New York City, publisher and bookseller, flourished from about 1821 to 1830 and published various toy books and chapbooks. His locations in New York were, at different times, 386 Broadway, 148 Fulton Street, and 150 William Street. At the latter place in 1828 he published "The Extraordinary Life and Adventures of Robin Hood," a thirty-two page chapbook with a colored frontispiece. In 1830 he brought out, in forty-eight pages, also with a colored frontispiece, "The Seven Champions of Christendom," etc. W. Borradaile also of New York published a "Robin Hood" in 1823.

The firm of Samuel Wood & Sons of New York was founded in 1804 by Samuel Wood, who was born at Oyster Bay, Long Island, in 1760. A former school teacher, he entered upon bookselling and his first place of business was at 362 Pearl Street, then the center of the book trade in New York. Much of his stock had been purchased at auction and in addition to second-hand books, he sold paper stock, stationery and cotton goods. After a short time he installed a small printing plant in the rear of his store and began to publish what became a long series of juvenile booklets and primers. Some of these children's books he wrote himself and some were illustrated from wood cuts made by Dr. Alexander Anderson.

In 1810 he moved to a larger place at 357 Pearl Street and in 1815 two of his sons, John and Samuel S., joined him in a partnership. The firm name then became Samuel Wood & Sons. An agency was established in Baltimore, Md., at 212 Market Street in 1818, by Samuel S. Wood.

In 1817 another move took place and Samuel Wood & Sons established themselves at 261 Pearl Street. At this time one son, John, retired and another, William, was admitted to partnership. Their business increased and a five-story building was erected for them at 261 Pearl Street. In 1836 Samuel S. and William bought out the interest of their father who retired, and in 1856 the firm removed to 389 Broadway. Other changes took place and scientific and medical publications became their chief interests.

Richard B. Carter and Charles J. Hendee opened a bookstore at 135 Washington Street, Boston, in 1828, and styled themselves publishers, booksellers, and stationers. About four years later they bought out the bookstore of Richardson and Lord, next door to them; sold their retail department to Allen and Ticknor; and moved upstairs at 131 Washington Street. Some children's chapbooks were published by this firm.

Mahlon Day, who had a bookstore at 374 Pearl Street, New York, and at other locations also, was a printer, bookseller and publisher who flourished from about 1821 to 1836 and later. He issued many children's chapbooks as well as other books for children.

In the "Jack and the Beanstalk," brought out in 1837 by T. H. Carter of Boston, the version departs so widely from the original that nothing is left except the bare bean-stalk and a boy named Jack. This Jack was a good little boy who merely planted a bean that grew very high. And his climb up the stalk was for the purpose of making a pleasant journey. On the way up, "he sat down on one of the strong branches of his bean and took out of his pocket a large piece of bread and butter pinned up in a napkin,

and ate it very heartily. Then he wiped his mouth and put up his napkin, took his
hatchet in his hand and began again to climb." But wonder of wonders, when he arrived
at the top, this Jack found no castle, no giant, no magic harp. Instead he was delighted to discover a paper mill, a type foundry, and a printing house, all in full
blast. And he is then initiated into the mysteries of book making. The author of this
version must have been a printer whose idea of the world above the sky certainly was
prosaic. This same version was published again in Boston by W. J. Reynolds & Co., No.
20 Cornhill. Richard Marsh of 374 Pearl Street, New York, included "Jack and the Bean
Stalk" as one of his series of Marsh's New Picture Books, published about 1855.

In "Happy Little Edward, and his pleasant Rides and Rambles in the country"
illustrated with engravings by Anderson, published by S. Babcock of New Haven in 1850,
Edward Jones, the hero, is a good and happy little boy of four years, who is taken on a
trip to Massachusetts by his parents. Edward has a fine time dipping his fingers into
a stream of water, smelling flowers, looking at squirrels and woodpeckers, meeting his
cousins, visiting rabbits and chickens, chasing butterflies and scampering about the
fields. Edward was delighted with the scenery on the trip, especially the river, "smooth
and shining like gold" at sunset. When Edward returned home, his dog Romeo barked and
wagged his tail and looked as pleased as Edward.

A curious conglomeration is found in the "Natural History of Animals" published
in 1839 at Concord, by Boyd and White. Each of its sixteen little pages carries an
illustration followed by a few lines of text. Although supposed to be a natural history of animals, it contains a picture of a plow, a mill for grinding corn, a rocking
horse, a barrel, etc., as well as pictures of a few birds. Beneath a coat-of-arms, the
text reads "The lion and the unicorn are fighting for the crown; and the lion has chased
the unicorn all around the town. So doth the powerful oppress the feeble and weak, and
make them submit to their tyranical power." It is apparent that sometimes children's
chapbooks were put together hurriedly by very thoughtless persons.

Bailey and Noyes of Portland, Maine, printed, among other things, a series of
twelve little children's chapbooks, about 1860. These twelve little books, each of
sixteen pages, measuring $3\frac{5}{8}$ x $2\frac{1}{2}$ inches with their pale yellow, pink, purple, blue and
brown covers, seem to belong to the period when gentlemen did not smoke cigars in the
streets. Their titles are somewhat forbidding. "The Two Goats and the Sick Monkey,"
"The Shepherd Boy," "The Book of Riddles," "Little Frank's Almanack," "The Twelve Months
of the Year," "The Medley," etc. Even the woodcuts adorning their covers and profusely
illustrating their pages have a respectable air, - a pineapple, a windmill, a beehive,
a cow, a horse, a tent, and so on - all belonging to a stiff, starchy Sunday afternoon.
"The Medley" is concerned with little tales about anchors, flags, tents, clocks, and
windmills in and near Boston, and in addition, the habit of early to bed and early to
rise is impressed upon the small readers.

Apparently it was not a criminal offence to mention ale and beer in children's
books about 1860. Among the riddles in "The Book of Riddles" are the following:

It foams without anger,
It flies without wings,
It cuts without edge,
And without tongue it sings.

A Bottle of Ale.

My habitation's in a wood,
And I'm at any one's command:
I often do more harm than good
If I once get the upper hand
I never fear the champion's frown,
Stout things I oftentimes have done;
Brave soldiers I have oft laid down,
I never fear their sword and gun.

A Barrel of Beer.

Some of the little chapbooks of this series were printed earlier than 1860 by other New England printers such as John F. Brown, Atwood & Brown, Moore's Power Press, and Rufus Merrill, all of Concord, N.H. Some of these, known as the "Concord Picture Books" contained some of the same woodcuts that appeared later in the Bailey and Noyes series.

These didactic little chapbooks lack the entertaining and amusing qualities of many of their relatives and I am sure that the children would have enjoyed them more had they contained a few Catnachian characteristics.

Chapter 25

SOME COLLECTORS AND COLLECTIONS

No less a person than James Boswell collected chapbooks, and his collection, bound in three small volumes with the title "Curious Productions," is housed in the Library of Harvard University, together with other chapbook collections, including those of Sir Alexander Boswell, William G. Medlicott of Springfield, Joseph Ritson, Bishop Percy, and others purchased and acquired in various ways, all of which were catalogued in their Bibliographical Contributions No. 56 entitled "Catalogue of English and American Chap-Books and Broadside Ballads in Harvard College Library," and published in 1905. This extensive and useful catalogue contains 2,461 entries, with very few duplicates. If the broadside ballads and a few other productions are subtracted, there is left about 1,650 actual chapbooks, and no doubt others have been acquired since the catalogue was published. In addition, the collection at Harvard includes examples in the Bohemian language, 1738-1863; Danish chapbooks, 1761-1870; Ductch ones of the early nineteenth century; some in Sicilian dialect, 1874-1894; and Swedish chapbooks, 1741-1868; as well as others in German and Italian.

About his chapbooks, James Boswell inserted a little autographed note in one of the volumes saying, "Having when a boy, been much interested with 'Jack the Giant Killer' and such little story books, I have always retained a kind of affection for them, as they recall my early days. I went to the printing office in Bow Churchyard and bought this collection and had it bound up with the title of 'Curious Productions.' I shall certainly, some time or other, write a little story book in the style of these. It will not be an easy task for me, it will require much nature and simplicity and a great acquaintance with the humors and traditions of the English common people. I shall be happy to succeed, for he who pleases children will be remembered with pleasure by men."

This collection by Boswell is representative as well as "curious" and having been made in Bow Churchyard in 1763, it contains imprints that are now scarce and highly desirable. Another famous collector, not of chapbooks, however, but of those interesting relatives of chapbooks, broadside ballads, was Samuel Pepys, whose collection was bequeathed to Magdalene College, Cambridge.

In 1925, a collection embracing 1,430 pieces (1698 to c. 1840) was offered for sale by Charles J. Sawyer of London. The nucleus of this was the famous Huth Collection, of 780 items, which was much enlarged after it changed hands in 1912. In addition the offering included chapbooks formerly in the possession of Motherwell and Fairley. According to Sawyer Darton in their "English Books 1475-1900," this collection of 1,430 chapbooks, including many desirable Aldermary imprints, came into the possession of Mr. Carl Pforzheimer. Mr. John A. Fairley of Edinburgh, a contributor to the literature of chapbooks, as well as a collector of note, gathered over a period of from thirty to forty years, one of, if not the finest collection of chapbooks ever brought together. Covering a period from the sixteenth to the nineteenth century and consisting of about 5,500 chapbooks (no duplicates) bound in 250 volumes, this collection was bequeathed in 1926 by Mr. and Mrs. W. R. Reid of Lauriston Castle to the National Library of Scotland. Various large and small, public and private collections of chapbooks exist in various cities in Great Britain and Europe, and it would be a difficult matter to take an accurate census of them. The British Museum must have a great number, although it would be difficult to pick them all out of their catalogue. The reference library of the Manchester Public Libraries has about 400 chapbooks of one sort or another, including many of Swindell's publications, and in addition, thirteen volumes containing 370 Italian chapbooks. The Edinburgh Public Libraries have a small collection. The Reference Department of the Birmingham Public Library possesses a small collection, most of them with Birmingham imprints, and in the University Library of Aberdeen there is a notable collection that was gathered together by Professor John Fraser. Mr. F. J. Harvey Darton, in his recent work, "Children's Books in England," states that the St. Bride's Institute Library, London, contains a large number of chapbooks.

In many libraries there is no way of distinguishing between chapbooks and other literature, and chapbooks are not kept by themselves. In the "Catalogue of the Bradshaw Collection of Irish Books in the University Library Cambridge," (1916) there are about 80 chapbook titles listed with Dublin imprints including many of Hannah More's Cheap Repository Tracts which many collectors classify as chapbooks.

R. S. Ferguson in the "Transactions of the Cumberland and Westmorland Antiquarian & Archaeological Society" for 1896 and 1900 gave a detailed list of some 233 chapbooks in the Bibliotheca Jacksoniana in Tullie House, Carlisle. These were from presses in 18 different towns and originally belonged to Mr. W. Jackson of Fleatham House, St. Bees.

Very recently (1936) The New York Public Library published a catalogue of their chapbooks, which covers a period ranging from about 1510 to 1850, with the majority consisting of English, Scotch and American chapbooks belonging to the first quarter of the nineteenth century. In their collection of approximately 1,200, the gems are the thirty Rappresentazioni Sacre and fifty-nine so-called Popular Tracts and Romances, printed in Italy during the sixteenth century and illustrated with Florentine woodcuts.

My friend and fellow-collector, Mr. Walter N. H. Harding of Chicago, who has been collecting chapbooks and songsters for many years, is the owner of an extensive and representative collection of over 6,000 different pieces, and his knowledge of them is extensive also. Mr. Harding's collection embraces garlands, songs, prose chapbooks with engraved frontispieces and colored plates, dramatic tales, juvenile dramas, English and American children's chapbooks, Cheap Repository Tracts and song books, and is, without doubt, the largest collection in America.

As has been noted, the American Antiquarian Society possesses the small but unique collection of Chapman Whitcomb's chapbooks. As chapbooks are not catalogued separately, there is no doubt that among its thousands of Colonial and later pamphlets, there are some that would qualify as chapbooks. And this statement is true also of its extensive collection of American children's books.

Mr. Valta Parma, former Curator, Rare Book Collection, of the Library of Congress, has gathered in the Rare Book Room about 700 chapbooks, the majority being English ones. These are representative of the output of different publishers, some of the eighteenth century, and the juvenile chapbooks include Banbury, York and other imprints. Such American chapbooks as have been gathered together include issues by B. & J. Johnson, N. Coverly, American Tract Society, etc. In addition there are Indian "Captivities" and chapbooks on "Crimes and Sufferings." There are many other chapbooks scattered throughout the Library of Congress, and once they are catalogued as such, their numbers and importance will be greatly augmented.

Sometimes auction and other catalogues contain lists of chapbooks and these are always a source of pleasure to collectors. The auction catalogue of the William Plumer library issued by C. F. Libbie & Co., of Boston, in 1910 lists many children's books including some chapbooks of New England, early nineteenth century origin. And the "Catalogue of the Books, Manuscripts and Maps relating principally to America collected by the late Levi Ziegler Leiter," which was privately printed in 1907 at Washington, D.C., includes a series of 344 Scottish chapbooks in twenty-two volumes. Just a year or so ago the Leiter library was sold at auction in New York City. One could, no doubt, upon further search, discover other collections of chapbooks which have long since been dispersed through auction and other sales. Nowadays book dealers' catalogues often contain a few stray titles, but for the most part, chapbooks have gravitated for some years towards a few public institutions and a few private collectors. Nowadays the collector has to sit like a spider in the center of a web and wait for chapbooks to appear. They can no longer be tracked down and captured.

Some persons have studied chapbooks closely and have traced many of the older tales to their probable sources. Some have studied them bibliographically. Some of these workers have been John Ashton, J. O. Halliwell-Phillipps, Rimbault, Clouston, George Lawrence Gomme, Baring-Gould, Henry B. Wheatley, John Fraser, John A. Fairley, Charles A. Federer, and R. S. Ferguson. Joseph Crawhall of Newcastle loved old chapbooks and reproduced many of them, and Mr. Andrew Tuer printed his work.

BIBLIOGRAPHY

ASHTON, JOHN. Chap-books of the eighteenth century. London: Chatto and Windus, 1882.

AXON, WILLIAM EDWARD ARMYTAGE. Some twentieth-century Italian chapbooks. (The Library. London, 1904, new series, v. 5, p. 239-255.)

BARNES, HENRY. On the McMechan chap-books in the Jackson Library, Carlisle. (Cumberland and Westmorland Antiquarian and Archaeological Society. Transactions. Kendal, 1917, new series, v. 17, p. 83-87.)

BERGENGREN, RALPH. Boswell's chapbooks and others. (The Lamp, New York, Feb. 1904.)

BLACK, GEORGE FRASER. A list of works relating to Scotland. New York, 1916. Chapbooks, p. 895-912.

BOEKENOOGEN, G. J. De Nederlandsche volksboeken. (Tijdschrift voor boek- en bibliotheekwezen. 's Gravenhage, 1905, jaarg, 3, p. 107-142.)

BRADLEY, WILL. Eighteenth century chapbooks and broadsides. (The American Chapbook. Sept., 1904, vol. 1, no. 1, p. 2-14.)

BROWN, ARTHUR C. L. The source of a Guy of Warwick chap-book. (Journal of Germanic philology. Bloomington, Ind., 1901, v. 3, p. 14-23.)

BROWN, REGINALD W. Northampton printing, printers and book-sellers (Jour. Northamptonshire Nat. His. Soc. and Field Club. Dec., 1918, vol. xix, No. 156, p. 1-30.)

CAMERON, ISABEL EDITH. A Highland chapbook. Stirling: E. Mackay [1928].

CATALOGUE OF THE BRADSHAW COLLECTION of Irish books in the university library Cambridge, vol. 1, Cambridge, University Library, 1916.

CATALOGUE OF A COLLECTION OF ENGLISH BALLADS of the xviith and xviiith Centuries. Bibliotheca Lindesiana, London, 1890.

CATALOGUE of English and American chapbooks and broadside ballads in Harvard college library, Cambridge, Mass., 1905. (Harvard College Library. Bibliographical contributions no. 56.)

CATALOGUE of the valuable library of the late William Plumer. C. F. Libbie & Co. Boston, 1910.

CHAMBERS, WILLIAM. Historical sketch of popular literature. A paper read before the Royal Society of Edinburgh, February 2, 1863.

CHAP-BOOKS and folk-lore tracts. First series. Edited by G. L. Gomme and H. B. Wheatley. London: Printed for the Villon Society, 1885, 5 v.
    v. i.　　The history of Thomas Hickathrift.
    v. ii.　 The history of the seven wise masters of Rome.
    v. iii. Mother Bunch's closet newly broke open.
    v. iv.　The history of patient Grisel.
    v. v.　　The history of Sir Richard Whittington.

CHENEY, C. R. Early Banbury chap-books and broadsides. (The Library, June, 1936, p. 98-109.)

CLARK, J. C. L. Notes on Chapman Whitcomb (Dartmouth 1785) eccentric poet and publisher of a scarce edition of Mrs. Rolandson's "Removes" and other Tracts. Lancaster, Mass., 1911. (Reprinted from the Clinton Daily Item.)

CUNNINGHAM, ROBERT HAYS, Editor. Amusing prose chap-books, chiefly of the last century.
     London: Hamilton, Adams & Co., 1889.

DARTON, F. J. HARVEY. Children's books in England. The Macmillan Company, Cambridge,
     1932, 360 p.

DE VINNE, THEODORE LOW. The chap-book and its outgrowths. (Literary collector. Green-
     wich, Conn., 1902, v. 5, p. 1-5.)

DUNCAN, WINTHROP H. Early american thrillers (The American Book Collector, Nov., Dec.,
     1932, vol. 2, nos. 5,6, p. 298-301, p. 355-359.)

----------. Josiah Priest historian of the American frontier. (Proc. Amer. Antiq. Soc.,
     April, 1934, 60 p.)

FAIRLEY, JOHN ALEXANDER. Chap-books & Aberdeen chap-books. Aberdeen: William Smith &
     Sons, The Bon-Accord Press, 1916.

     Dougal Graham and the chap-books by and attributed to him. Glasgow: J. Maclehose
     & Sons, 1914.

FEDERER, CHARLES A., Editor. Yorkshire chap-books. London: E. Stock, 1889.

FERGUSON, R. S. On the chap-books in the Bibliotheca Jacksonian in Tullie House, Car-
     lisle (Archaeological journal. London, 1895, v. 52 [Series 2, v. 2], p. 292-335.)

     On the collection of chap-books in the Bibliotheca Jacksoniana, in Tullie House,
     Carlisle, with some remarks on the history of printing in Carlisle, Whitehaven,
     Penrith, and other north country towns. (Cumberland and Westmorland Antiquarian
     & Archaeological Society. Transactions. Kendal, 1897-1900, v. 14, p. 1-120;
     v. 16, p. 56-79.)

FIELD, LOUISE FRANCES (Story). The child and his book. London: W. Gardner, Darton &
     Co., [1895] 2. ed.

FRASER, JOHN. The humorous chap-books of Scotland. New York: H. L. Hinton, 1873-[74].
     2 v.

GENT, THOMAS. The life of Mr. Thomas Gent, printer, of York; written by himself. Lon-
     don: Printed for Thomas Thorpe, 1832.

GERRING, CHARLES. Notes on printers and booksellers; with a chapter on chap books.
     London: Simpkin, Marshall, Hamilton, Kent & Co., Ltd., 1900.

GRAHAM, DOUGAL. The collected writings of Dougal Graham. Edited, with notes...by
     George MacGregor. Glasgow: T. D. Morrison, 1883, 2 v.

GREEN, EMANUAL. Cheap repository tracts (Bibliotheca Somersetensis, vol. 3, p. 64-94.)

HALLIWELL-PHILLIPPS, JAMES ORCHARD. A catalogue of chap-books, garlands, and popular
     histories, in the possession of James Orchard Halliwell, Esq. London: For private
     circulation, 1849.

     Descriptive notices of popular English histories. (In: Percy Society. Early
     English poetry. London, 1848, v. 23, [no.3].)

     Notices of fugitive tracts, and chap-books. 1849. (In: Percy Society. Early
     English poetry. London, 1851, v. 29, [no. 5].)

HARVEY, WILLIAM. Scottish chapbook literature. Paisley: A. Gardner, 1903.

HEARTMAN, CHARLES FREDERICK. Checklist of printers in the United States, from Stephen
     Daye to the close of the War of Independence. New York City [1915]. (Heartman's
     historical series, no. 9.)

HINDLEY, CHARLES. "The Catnach Press." A collection of the books and woodcuts of
     James Catnach, late of Seven Dials, printer. [Compiled by Charles Hindley.]
     London: Reeves and Turner [1869].

The history of the Catnach Press. London: C. Hindley <the younger>, 1887.

HINDLEY, CHARLES. A History of the cries of London. London, Reeves and Turner, 1881, 272 p.

JEWITT, LLEWELLYN. Art among the ballad mongers. (The Art Journal, London, vol. xvii, 1878, ns. p. 17-20; 41-44; 229-232; vol. xviii, 1879, n.s. p. 69-72; 157-160; 185-188.)

JORDAN, CARYL. Of broadsides and chapbooks. (World's work. London, 1914, v. 23, p. 286-291.)

JORDAN, PHILIP D. and DANIEL C. HASKELL. The Juvenilia of Mary Belson Elliott. New York Public Library, New York, 1936, 18p.

KIDSON, FRANK. The Ballad sheet and garland (Jour. Folk-Song Society, 1905, vol. 2, pt. 2, no. 7, p. 70-78.)

KING, L. MELTON. What is a chap-book? (London Magazine, vol. xiii, no. 76, p. 457-461.)

KOPP, ARTHUR. Niederdeutsche Liederdrucke aus dem 16. Jahrhundert. (Centralblatt für Bibliothekswesen. Leipzig, 1902. Jahrg. 19, p. 509-529.)

MABBOTT, THOMAS OLIVE. Two chapbooks printed by Andrew Steuart. (The American book collector. Metuchen, N.J., 1933, v. 3, p. 325-328.)

MACLAGAN, P. J. Notes on some Chinese chap-books. (The China review. Hongkong, 1897-98, v. 22, p. 782-786; v. 23, p. 163-167.)

MORRISON, HUGH A. The Leiter library, a catalogue, etc. Washington, D.C., 1907.

NISARD, CHARLES. Histoire des livres populaires: ou, de la littérature du colportage, depuis le xve siecle jusqu'a l'établissement de la Commission d'examen des livres du colportage. Paris: Amyot, 1854, 2 v.

OLD JEST BOOKS. (The Strand Magazine, vol. 15, p. 295-304.)

ONE HUNDRED YEARS OF PUBLISHING. New York, William Wood and Company, 1904, 30 p.

PEARSON, EDWIN. Banbury chap books. London: A. Reader, 1890, obl.

PETSCH, ROBERT. Das Rockenbuchlein. (Zeitschrift für Bücherfreunde Bielefeld, 1901. Jahrg. 5, p. 35-37.)

PYLE, HOWARD. Chapbook heroes (Harper's new monthly magazine. New York, 1890, v. 81, p. 123-138.)

ROCK, W. H. Swindell's penny histories. (Manchester Guardian, Nov. 16, 1874.)

ROSENBACH, ABRAHAM S. WOLF. Early American children's books. Portland, Maine: The Southworth Press, 1933.

SIEVEKING, I. GIBERNE. The mediaeval chapbook as an educational factor in the past. (The Reliquary. London, 1903, new series, v. 9, p. 241-252.)

SMITH, CLARA A. Narratives of captivity among the indians of North America, and Suppl. I. The Newberry Library, Chicago, Ill.

TAPLEY, HARRIET SILVESTER. History of the first fifty years of printing in Salem, Massachusetts, Salem, 1927.

VAIL, R. W. G. The Abraham panther indian captivity. (The Amer. Book Collector, 1932, vol. 2, nos. 2,3, p. 165-172, Aug., Sept.)

WATT, WILLIAM WHYTE. Shilling shockers of the gothic school. Cambridge, Mass.: Harvard University Press, 1932. (Harvard honors theses in English, no. 5.)

WEISS, HARRY B. Alexander Wilson as a chapbook author. (Amer. Book Collector, Oct., 1932, vol. 2, no. 4, p. 218-219.)

WEISS, HARRY B. American chapbooks, 1938. Privately printed, 31 pages, 3 plates, 100 copies.

----------. American editions of Sir Richard Whittington and his cat. (Bull. New York Public Library, June 1938, vol. 42, no. 6, p. 477-485.)

----------. The Autochthonal tale of jack the giant killer (Scientific Monthly, Feb., 1929, vol. 28, p. 126-133.)

----------. A Catalogue of the chapbook in the New York Public Library, New York, 1936, 90 p.

----------. A Chapbook on natural history. (The Amer. Collector, Feb. 1928, vol. 5, p. 212-214.)

----------. Chapman Whitcomb, early American publisher and peddler of chapbooks. (Book Collectors' Packet, April, 1939, vol. 3, no. 8, p. 1-3.)

----------. The charms of chapbooks. (The American Book Collector. Metuchen, N.J., 1932, v. 1, p. 166-169.)

----------. The Deathless dairyman's daughter. (The Amer. Collector, Mar. 1928, vol. 5, no. 6, p. 250-252.)

----------. English and American valentine writers. (Bull. New York Public Library, Feb., 1939, vol. 43, no. 2, p. 71-86.)

----------. The Ephemeral comic valentine. (The Amer. Collector. July-Aug., 1928, vol. 6, nos. 3-4, p. 98-110.)

----------. Jack and the bean-stalk, a publisher's version. (Book Collectors' Packet. Nov., 1938, vol. 3, no. 3, p. 6-7.)

----------. John Norman, engraver, publisher, bookseller, etc. (Bull. New York Public Library, Jan., 1934, vol. 38, no. 1, p. 3-14.)

----------. John Turner of Coventry. (Amer. Book Collector, April, 1935, p. 141-142.)

----------. Little red riding hood, a terror tale of the nursery, 1939. Privately printed, 19 pages, frontis., 100 copies.

----------. Mahlon Day, early New York printer, bookseller and publisher of children's books. (Bull. New York Public Library, Dec., 1941, vol. 45, no. 12, p. 1007-1021.)

----------. The Pennsylvania hermit. (The Amer. Collector, Dec., 1927, vol. 5, no. 3, p. 114-117.)

----------. Something about Simple Simon. (Bull. New York Public Library, June, 1940, vol. 44, no. 6, p. 461-470.)

----------. Three hundred years of Tom Thumb. (The Scientific Monthly, 1932, vol. 34, p. 157-166.)

----------. Twelve toy books of the past mid-century. (The Amer. Book Collector, Feb., 1932, vol. 1, no. 2, p. 91-93.)

----------. The Way to wealth and other franklin chapbooks. (Amer. Book Collector, May-June, 1935, p. 193-195.)

----------. Williap Cowper's frolic in rhyme. The diverting history of John Gilpin. (Bull. New York Public Library, Sept. 1937, vol. 41, no. 9, p. 675-680.)

----------. The "wonderful discovery of a hermit," a best seller in 1786. (Book Collectors' Packet, Dec., 1939, vol. 3, no. 11, p. 1-3.)

WELFORD, RICHARD. Early Newcastle typography. (Archaeologia Aeliana, vol. 3, Ser. 3, p. 18-23; p. 39-41; p. 124.)

WILLIAMS, JOHN CAMP. An Oneida county printer; William Williams, printer, publisher, editor. New York: C. Scribner's Sons, 1906.

WINSLOW, OLA ELIZABETH. Amerian broadside verse. Yale Univ. Press, New Haven, Conn. 1930.

WRIGHT, RICHARDSON. Hawkers and walkers in early America. J. B. Lippincott Company, Philadelphia, Pa., 1927.

ADDENDUM

BLAND, DESMOND SPARLING. Chapbooks and Garlands in the Robert White Collection in the Library of King's College, Newcastle Upon Tyne. Newcastle Upon Tyne, 1956.

JOHN CHENEY AND HIS DESCENDENTS, Printers in Banbury Since 1767. Banbury, 1936. (Appendix II, an inventory of chapbooks, broadsides, etc. Appendix III, a short-title list of chap-books, broadsides, etc.)

CROPPER, PERCY J. The Nottinghamshire Printed Chap-Books, with notices of Their Printers and Vendors. Illustrated. Nottingham, 1892 (Only known copy in British Museum.)

JENNINGS, JOHN MELVILLE. The Poor Unhappy Transported Felon's Sorrowful Account of His Fourteen Years Transportation at Virginia in America. (Virginia Magazine of History and Biography, April, 1948, Vol. 56, No. 2, p. 180-194.)

NEUBURG, VICTOR E. Chapbooks: A Bibliography of References to English and American Chap-book Literature of the Eighteenth and Nineteenth Centuries. London: The Vine Press, 1964.

SHEPARD, LESLIE. The Broadside Ballad, A Study in Origins and Meaning. London: Herbert Jenkins, and Hatboro, Pa.: Folklore Associates, 1962. (Illustrations of chapbooks, garlands, and tracts, p. 130-134.)

WEISS, HARRY B. Early American Chapbooks. (The American Collector, December, 1944, Vol. 13, No. 11, p. 10-11.)

----------. Hannah More's Cheap Repository Tracts in America. (Bulletin New York Public Library, July, 1946, Vol. 50, No. 7, p. 539-549; August, 1946, Vol. 50, No. 8, p. 634-641.)

----------. Oneirocritica Americana [American Dream Books]. (Bulletin New York Public Library, June, 1944, Vol. 48, No. 6, p. 519-541, 1 plate; July, 1944, Vol. 48, No. 7, p. 642-653.)

----------. Samuel Wood and Sons, Early New York Publishers of Children's Books. (Bulletin New York Public Library, September, 1942, Vol. 46, No. 9, p. 755-771, 1 pl.)

----------. Solomon King, Early New York Publisher of Children's Books and Chapbooks. (Bulletin New York Public Library, September, 1947, Vol. 51, No. 9, p. 531-544.)

At the Wish of the Fish

A RUSSIAN FOLKTALE

adapted by **J. Patrick Lewis**

illustrated by **Katya Krénina**

ATHENEUM BOOKS FOR YOUNG READERS

For Karen, John, and Caroline Angell
—J. P. L.

For Reni, Frank, and Tommy, with love
—K. K.

Author's Note

This story is based on a Russian folktale, "Po shchuch'emu velen'yu" ("At the Will of the
Pike"). It appears in *Russkiye Narodniye Skazki (Popular Russian Folktales)*, Moscow:
Gosudarstvennoye Izdatel'stvo Detskoi Literatury, 1958. The tale was originally told by
Alexander Afanas'ev (1826-1871).

I have taken liberties with the literal translation—hence, this is an adaptation rather than a
mere retelling, and I have given the tale a more childlike title.

—J. P. L.

Atheneum Books for Young Readers
An imprint of Simon & Schuster Children's Publishing Division
1230 Avenue of the Americas
New York, New York 10020
Text copyright © 1999 by J. Patrick Lewis
Illustrations copyright © 1999 by Katya Krénina
All rights reserved, including the right of reproduction in whole or
in part in any form.
Book design by Angela Carlino
The text of this book is set in Triplex Serif Light.
The illustrations are rendered in watercolor and gouache.
First Edition
Printed in Hong Kong
10 9 8 7 6 5 4 3 2 1

Library of Congress Cataloging-in-Publication Data: Lewis, J. Patrick.
At the wish of the fish ; an adaptation of a Russian folktale / by J.
Patrick Lewis ; illustrated by Katya Krénina.—1st ed.
p. cm.
Based on the Russian folktale "Po shchuch'emu velen'yu."
Summary: In this adaptation of a traditional Russian tale, a lazy fool
catches an enchanted fish that promises him that every wish he ever
makes will come true.
ISBN 0-689-81336-8
[1. Fairy tales. 2. Folklore—Russia.] I. Afanas'ev, A. N. (Aleksandr
Nikolaevich), 1826-1871. II. Krénina, Katya, ill.
III. Po shchuch'emu velen'yu. IV. Title.
PZ8.L48116At 1999
398.2'0947'02—dc21 [E] 97-42238 CIP AC

Once, long ago, in a kingdom beyond blue kingdoms, there lived three brothers. The first two were clever lads, riding off to the Suzdal Fair to trade their wares. The youngest brother, Emelya, was a simpleton, a silly goose, a pancake—take your pick, he was all three in one.

"We will be gone for a month, Emelya," said the two older brothers. "While we're away, listen to our wives and obey their every command. If you do as you're told, a new red caftan, red boots, and a red hat will be your reward."

"A red caftan!" Emelya shouted from his usual spot on top of his beloved broken-down stove, which stood in the corner collecting cobwebs. (So simple was he that he thought it kept him warm.) Almost immediately he fell back to sleep.

A day passed, two days, then a week. "Get up off that stove, Emelya!" his sisters-in-law cried. "Fetch us some water, you lazyboots!"

"I don't want to," Emelya replied sleepily. "I'm comfortable right where I am."

"There'll be no red caftan for you . . . unless you fetch us some water for our cooking. Wait till our husbands hear this!"

"What a bother to be out in the cold," Emelya grumbled to himself as he gathered up two pails and an axe and trudged down the hill to the lake. There, he whacked a hole in the ice and lowered his bucket into the water. "Oh, oh, oh!" he exclaimed. "Look at the pike that's jumped into my pail! Won't I be eating a tasty fish soup for my dinner!"

"Wait," said the frisky pike. "If you throw me back in and let me swim free, I'll give you anything you desire."

"I'm not the brightest fellow in the world," Emelya laughed, "but this sounds like a trick!"

"No trick. Just say my name," the pike explained, "and whatever you wish for shall be yours."

So Emelya said: "By the will of the pike, do as I like. Send my pails back home all by themselves." Instantly the two buckets galloped up the hill, where the villagers stood gawking at the sight. The pails ran all the way home and into the cottage without spilling a drop.

Now, time passed and the moss grew. But which one the faster, who could say? "Emelya, winter is still beating at the door," the sisters-in-law shouted. "Go to the forest and bring back a sleighful of kindling. Otherwise, you'll be lucky to see that red caftan in your dreams."

Emelya did as he was told. He heaved two axes and a coil of rope into the sleigh, and pushed the sleigh into the snow. Jumping up on the seat, he shouted to the women to open the gate. They did so, all the while waiting for more foolishness to billow forth from his lips.

"How can you go anywhere, you fool?" they laughed. "You haven't hitched up the horse!"

"Who needs a horse?" he replied. "At the pike's request, the sleigh runs west." And so it did, racing through the village so fast that the peasants had no time to get out of the way!

"Slow down, watch out!" they shouted, but the horseless sleigh flew on and on.

Finally alone in the silent wood, Emelya cried out, "If it please the pike, let the axes strike. Come out of the forest, ice bear, and tie the logs into small bundles." Just so, the two axes fell on the trees, one at the roots and one at the branches. And suddenly there he was, a giant ice bear neatly stacking the logs in the sleigh without so much as a growl.

Emelya returned home the way he came, but this time the villagers were waiting for him. They would have thrashed him soundly, too, but he said, "In the pike's good name, four clubs take aim!" Magically, four logs broke free of the rope and raised themselves up out of the sleigh, threatening to wallop anyone who harmed the driver. Emelya sped safely home, climbed up on the stove, and fell fast asleep.

It wasn't long before the Tsar heard from the angry peasants about the silly goose who flew through the snow on a horseless sleigh, scattering citizens hither and yon. So he ordered a regiment of his Imperial Guards to fetch Emelya and bring him to the palace at once. When they arrived at the cottage, the commanding officer said in a gruff voice, "Get up, good-for-nothing. You are wanted at the Tsar's palace."

"I would rather stay here, thank you," Emelya said. "My stove is all the comfort I need."

The officer was about to cuff him across the ear when Emelya wished, "If the pike can hear, make them disappear. Back to the Tsar who sent them."

Poof! The entire regiment flew away in a flash! And soon they stood, dazed and silent, before the Tsar. "What's this?" His Majesty exclaimed, amazed that Emelya could have vanquished so many men. "Perhaps the simpleton isn't so simple after all. This time I will send the wisest man in the kingdom to fetch the fool. With trickery, if need be."

A week later, the wise man came upon Emelya's sisters-in-law feeding the chickens in the yard. "Tell me what he likes the most," he whispered.

"Foolish Emelya loves nothing but the old woodstove he sleeps on," the first one said. "That and the promise of a new red caftan, red boots, and a red hat," the second one laughed.

Ah, thought the wise man, as he entered the cottage. "Come with me to the Tsar's palace, my fine fellow, and you shall have a brand-new suit of clothes. Red from toes to crown!"

Emelya agreed, but he said, "You go along, and I will follow after." Then he sat for awhile on top of his stove, thinking this and wondering that. "If the pike's nearby, let this woodstove fly. Take me to the Tsar!"

No sooner had he spoken than the roof rattled, the walls shook, and the dusty stove bolted out the door, through the trees, and into the sky. Leaning out the palace window, the Tsar saw the fool and his stove come flying toward him at breakneck speed!

"Emelya the Simpleton," the Tsar roared, as the stove landed right on top of the courtyard statue of the Tsar himself. "You knocked over half a village on your horseless sleigh. What do you have to say for yourself?"

"Forgive me, Your Highness, should I have asked them to get out of the way?" Emelya asked, scratching his head. At that moment he looked up and saw for the first time the beautiful Tsarevna Marya in the uppermost window. "At the pike's pleasure, bring me this treasure," he said softly. "Let the Tsar's daughter fall in love with me."

Faster than a mouse on a cat's watch, Marya ran down the stairs and into the yard and begged her father to let her marry Emelya. The Tsar raged at the very thought of his own daughter wanting to wed the flying fool. "You have disgraced the royal house, Marya. And you . . . you simpleton scoundrel!" the Tsar bellowed. "Seize him!"

Emelya was so dazzled by the Tsarevna's beauty that he did not even think to ask the pike to help him escape. The Tsar ordered that Emelya and Marya be stuffed into a huge barrel wrapped with an iron band. Quickly, the guards followed orders, sealed the barrel with tar, and cast it out to sea.

Now, the dark inside the barrel and the gentle lapping of the waves soon put Emelya to sleep. But hours later, hunger woke him. "Where am I?" he asked. Someone was sobbing next to him. "And who are you?" Emelya whispered, for he could not see a thing in the pitch-black barrel.

"Oh, my beloved Emelyushka, don't you remember? I am Marya, the Tsar's daughter," she said, overcome by the fate that had befallen them. "How shall we ever get out of this barrel?"

Touched by the Tsarevna's tears, Emelya said, "By the pike's command, let us find dry land, and not too far away from the Tsar. Break apart, barrel, as soon as we are safe."

Whoosh! A giant wave flung the barrel up on a green and wild shore. *Craaack!* went the barrel, and out stepped the young couple. "Could you find us something to eat, Emelyushka," Marya begged, "and build us a little hut to keep the rain away?"

"Dear pike, most loyal, may life be royal. With a house full of food . . . and a fool's gratitude."

The pike must have been feeling especially generous, for what was once the windy shore became a palace so grand that even the Tsar himself would not believe it. Inside, Marya and Emelya gazed at the riches before them!

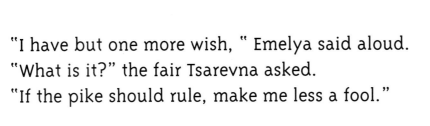

"I have but one more wish, " Emelya said aloud.
"What is it?" the fair Tsarevna asked.
"If the pike should rule, make me less a fool."

Instantly, Emelya turned into a dashing noble, handsome as a prince, clever as a duke.

"Go to the Tsar," Emelya told a servant, "and invite him to dinner at our palace."

The servant arrived at the royal court and delivered the message.

"Who is your master?" said the Tsar.

"That is a mystery, Your Majesty, but you will find out soon enough."

So the royal party mounted their horses and rode to Emelya's grand palace. Such splendor they had never seen before.

Emelya welcomed the Tsar. "Do you know who I am, Your Majesty?"

"By the moon and stars, my dear Prince, I have never seen you before."

"Have you forgotten the fool on the flying stove?" And as he said these words, Emelya led the Tsar's daughter into the room.

So great was His Majesty's shock and shame that he knelt before his daughter. "Forgive me, dearest Marya, for my ignorance. I have done you a great injustice, Emelya. You shall have my daughter's hand in marriage—and a wedding fit for a king."

But Emelya insisted that his brothers and sisters-in-law and all manner of common folk be invited to the glorious ball under the chandeliers. There, prince and peasant, rich and poor, ate and drank and danced till dawn.

Though Emelya and Marya lived for many years in that peaceful kingdom, the once-upon-a-time simpleton never forgot the great good fortune bestowed upon him by the pike. And often he was heard to say, as he strolled through the gardens in his princely red caftan,

"By the will of a fish, I have done all I wish."